The Boyne Valley in the Ice Age

A Field Guide to Some of the Valley's Most Important Glacial Geological Features

By
Robert T. Meehan
and
William P. Warren

Published jointly by Meath County Council
and the Geological Survey of Ireland

Design and Layout by Cartography Unit

Printed in Ireland by Betaprint

ISBN 1-899702-20-2

© Geological Survey of Ireland 1999

Acknowledgements

This book is a product of co-operative work between Meath County Council and the Geological Survey of Ireland and we wish to thank all those in both organisations who co-operated in and supported its production. In particular we would like to acknowledge the enthusiasm and vision shown by Oliver Perkins, the County Engineer who initially proposed that the work be undertaken and supported it throughout. Thanks also to Bríd O'Connell at Meath Tourism Ltd. for her continued encouragement and support. Meath Tourism Ltd. also provided two photographs, one of Tara Hill (Cover, p. 19) and Newgrange (p. 8). The cartographic staff at the Geological Survey of Ireland for the setup, design and layout. Thanks are also due to Dr. Colman Gallagher and Dr. Peter O' Connor for use of parts of their respective photo collections. Finally, thanks to the people of Meath for their help, kindness, interest, good natured humour and wit over the three years of fieldwork preceding the production of this guide: hoping you enjoy this booklet and that it somehow spurs an even greater interest in the landscape of this beautiful county.

Table of Contents

Preface

The Valley of the Boyne is one of Ireland's most renowned tourist attractions for a variety of reasons. Its proximity to Dublin and its rich endowments of heritage features have rendered it a popular destination for both day trippers and longer stay visitors. The archaeological monuments of the area are well known and many are of prime international significance (the Brú na Boinne Complex has been designated a World Heritage Site by UNESCO), others such as the Round Tower complex at Kells are of national importance while smaller sites provide curiosities at the local level. The Boyne Valley has long been the focus of tours by visitors at every level of interest including casually curious visitors, school groups of all ages, university groups from history, geography and archaeology departments and both national and international groups of academics attached to these disciplines. The archaeological sites reflect the complex history of the people who lived in this area since the Neolithic (late Stone Age) period. It should be remembered that all of the sites on which these monuments occur were chosen as a result of their size, shape or position in the landscape. The purpose of this book is to illustrate the nature of the critical landscape features in the area and their relationship to the prehistoric and historic human monuments, in other words we have set out to investigate the impact of the geology and geomorphology (surface shape) on the evolution of the human landscape.

This guide stems from research that was carried out between 1993 and 1996 into the Quaternary Geology of County Meath. Most of the research was carried out by the Geological Survey of Ireland for Meath County Council as one of the main components of a Groundwater Protection Scheme for the county. The resulting map illustrated the distribution of surface sediments from the point of view of natural resources and foundation conditions for major civil engineering undertakings. A map which outlines the nature of the surface sediments of the county as well as the landscape, or geomorphologic, elements formed the main component of the research results.

The County Engineer, Oliver Perkins, saw immediately the potential of this research to form the basis upon which an illustration of the chief natural heritage features of the Boyne Valley area could be constructed. Thus was the idea for this book engendered.

The geological foundations of the Boyne Valley landscape were formed over a period of 500 million years. The broad shape of the countryside emerged during the latter part of the Tertiary Period (2 - 60 million years ago) but the final touches were put to the emerging physical landscape during the ice ages of the past 1.65 million years, in particular the last great ice age which ended 10,000 years ago. The first section of the booklet details a number of 'tours' which have been formulated, with a guide to selected features of interest, many of which lie close to the archaeological attractions. The second section of the guide deal with this ice age and glaciation in general, as well as the way in which glacial ice moulded the Irish landscape. A description of the solid rock base in the valley, is provided as well as the effects of the ice age on the landscape of the area. As the valley is a mosaic of features of different age, the varying ages of features are examined in some detail.

Within this guide the Boyne Valley area is taken to cover the entire catchment of the Boyne River. Some of the tours extend outside this, and reference is made to some sites just outside the confines of the catchment. It is hoped that the guide will help create a better understanding and appreciation of glacial landforms and the diverse processes that have affected the Irish landscape. It should help people realise that the landscape, howsoever banal, contains within it a long, varied and vibrant history reflecting intense processes which have operated for a time much longer and at a scale much larger than human existence.

The Boyne Valley: Geological Tours

These tours are designed with specific beginning and end points but one may begin and end as the fancy takes and circumstances permit. The Ordnance Survey's 1:50,000 scale maps of the area are recommended and the area is covered by four sheets (35, 42, 43 and 49). The 1:126,720 (1/2 inch to 1 mile) map (sheet 13) is however quite adequate and it covers the whole area of the Boyne valley tours. Following this section (the guided tours), the processes by which the Great Ice Ages put the finishing touches on the landscape are described. In addition, a glossary of technical terms used is added.

Today we tend to take our location in the landscape for granted. The site of our suburban house was probably determined by happenstance and controlled only by planning regulations. This is true also of many other types of modern buildings: schools, churches, offices etc. The location is usually determined by land availability and planning controls. Not so in the past. Our ancestors read the landscape and chose important sites very carefully and deliberately. We will find humble cabins of a few centuries past built snugly in the shelter of esker ridges and Norman moats (motte) on well-chosen hill tops such as kames or moraines (e.g. Navan Moat)

There are many excellent guides to the archaeological sites of County Meath but here we attempt an explanation of the glacial features of the Boyne valley and many of the historical sites, which were always very carefully chosen. An understanding of the nature of the situation of an ancient site will help to appreciate the reasons for choosing it and often the mind-set of those who chose it.

Many archaeological monuments were built on specifically glacial features - relics of the Ice Age - and all were built in a landscape that in its detail is a product of the Ice Age.

1

Good views of glacial features can be had from many of the archaeological sites in the Boyne Valley. Additionally, many glaciated features in the region can also be appreciated from roadside localities. This part of the booklet is a guide to a number of tours which introduce and highlight the most exciting glacial sites in the region. It explains in particular, the importance of the last ice age in the evolution of today's landscape and how the scenery was shaped during the Ice Age. Each tour visits numerous sites and also describes the journey between them. Each site has been given a national grid reference which details a convenient access point to view the feature. In appreciating the scenery of the area try to imagine the amount of time needed for the ice to have moulded the landscape by erosion of material and its subsequent deposition (in order to imagine this consider a glacier moving at a rate of 5 cm per day would be regarded as fast-moving compared to parts of the Antarctic ice sheet which move at only 5 cm per year).

While driving along the routes please pay attention to other drivers (especially those behind you!) if driving slowly. Extra care should be taken when parking at the roadside as some of the roads are quite narrow and have a heavy flow of traffic. Access to gravel pits is by permission of the owners or operators and their advice on safety must be followed.

Touring Route 1: The Lower Boyne Valley (Drogheda to Navan).

Driving between Drogheda and Mellifont

Leaving Drogheda the most striking components of the landscape are the very steep flanks of the Boyne Channel which reflect glaciofluvial erosion during the deglacial period. The waters of the Boyne River in the deglacial times actually filled most of the valley in this locality, such were the volumes of water generated by the melting ice sheets. This means that most of present day Drogheda would have been under water at that time.

The road to Mellifont passes the Mell Quarries, from which limestone has been extracted for many decades. The limestone in this area is karstified and some caverns can be seen deep in the quarry. From the road several metres of glacial till can be seen resting on the limestone bedrock. Past the quarry, looking south from the road, the horizon is dominated by the Platin Cement Works, which also utilises the pure limestone of the area. West of the chimneys at the works, the rounded ridge at Donore and the flat-topped Redmountain Hill protrude above the gently undulating valley surrounds. Closer to Mellifont on the northern side of the road the high hills of Glassallen and Starinagh are cored by Silurian age rocks and have been rounded by ice. You can park your car in the car park at the Abbey. Notice the deep channel in which the abbey lies and the craggy surrounding hills.

Steep valley sides suggesting the depth of water in the Boyne Channel during deglaciation, Drogheda.

Site 1: Mellifont Abbey (NGR 3012 2781)

Mellifont Abbey was, in medieval times, the centre of the Cistercian Order and a building of exceptional beauty and grandeur. Founded in 1142, it was the first Cistercian Monastery in Ireland and flourished for nearly 400 years, presiding over up to 38 monasteries throughout Ireland.

Mellifont Abbey is built in the centre of a meltwater channel which was cut by water flowing into the Boyne Glaciofluvial System during deglaciation. This not only provided a level site for the building, it also provided fertile land and the channel side gave shelter to the monastery. The channel is cut into bedrock and till and now provides a course for the Mattock River. Bedrock crops out in some places along the base of the channel (notably, just inside the Abbey itself) and consists of Lower Palaeozoic age siltstone which

Mellifont Abbey, situated in the centre of the Mattock Meltwater Channel.

has been intensely altered (hence the cross cutting joints present in the outcrops and the 'slanted' beds visible in the outcrops along the side of the channel). These outcrops on the side of the channel are generally polished and smooth on top, but are jagged on their southern sides. This is a product of ice - polishing and ice-plucking during glaciation.

The base of the stream predominantly exposes till which can be seen lying unevenly over bedrock in some localities. The till is a rusty colour and looks like a fruit cake with dark stones in a matrix of orange clay. The rusty colour comes from the weathering of minerals in the deposit, the most important of which is iron.

Driving between Mellifont and the Boyne battlefield

The road crossing Louth Hill provides an excellent view of the Upper Boyne Valley. All of this landscape was smothered by ice several hundred metres thick during the Ice Age. The immediate area has some small crags of bedrock protruding above the soil: this is similar to many of the high ridges in the area, where the ice has eroded the bedrock but has deposited little debris. Leaving Louth Hill the road descends eastwards into King William's Glen at Tullyallen. This is a meltwater channel which was cut into the local bedrock by very powerful water flows at the end of the ice age. While driving through the channel we are in effect leaving the moulded rock surface of the hills and entering the Boyne Gorge which was gouged out by both ice and water during the Ice Age. It should be remembered that the gorge itself was eroded out of bedrock and then partly infilled with glacial till and finally glaciofluvial gravels.

At the southern end of the glen walk to the viewing point taking in the Boyne Battlefield. From here you will see terraces associated with different levels of the deglacial Boyne.

Site 2: King William's Glen viewing point (NGR 3045 2766)

The tract of land below the viewing point was the setting for the Battle of the Boyne in 1690. This was fought between the armies of the English King James II and his son in law William and decided the future of Ireland, the English Crown and the European balance of power. William, attacking from the north, succeeded in crossing the river and routing James' army which had held a strong position on the southern side.

This viewing point is a good place to visualise the scale of the Boyne River during deglacial times. On the south side of the river (opposite bank) a well developed, flat-topped terrace can be seen to the right of the Obelisk Bridge. This terrace represents the river floodplain during deglaciation. The water would therefore have almost reached as high as the point at which you are standing. Since deglaciation the river has cut its way down to the modern floodplain which can clearly be seen at the base of the valley. Looking towards Oldbridge some well drained hillocks can be seen at a level above the Boyne deglacial river (some of these are covered in furze bushes). These hummocks are kames which were deposited by ice. Some small disused pits are present at Oldbridge, showing the presence of well sorted, poorly bedded gravels and sands. Some erratics of volcanic rock

The view from the Battle of the Boyne viewing point, showing the wide floodplain and flanking terraces of the Boyne.

from the Mourne Mountains are present. This indicates that ice flow over the area was generally north to south and was influenced by the ice sheet in the Irish Sea Basin.

Driving between King William's Glen and Newgrange

Pass over the Obelisk Bridge and follow the road to the top of Sheephouse Hill. The roads first follows the boundary between the alluvium and the gravel before turning southwards up the hill. The road at Sheephouse passes a limestone quarry which records the presence of rock close to the surface in this area. However, most of the best agricultural fields in this area are underlain by glacial till, resulting in deep topsoil and supporting rich pasture. Driving through Donore Village the road

passes between Donore Hill and Redmountain, both have been shaped by ice. The road then enters the Stalleen Meltwater Channel (note the steep slopes on both sides) which was cut at the end of the last deglaciation by another tributary river of the Boyne. Dowth and Newgrange can now be seen and you can park your car in the car park at Brú na Bóinne.

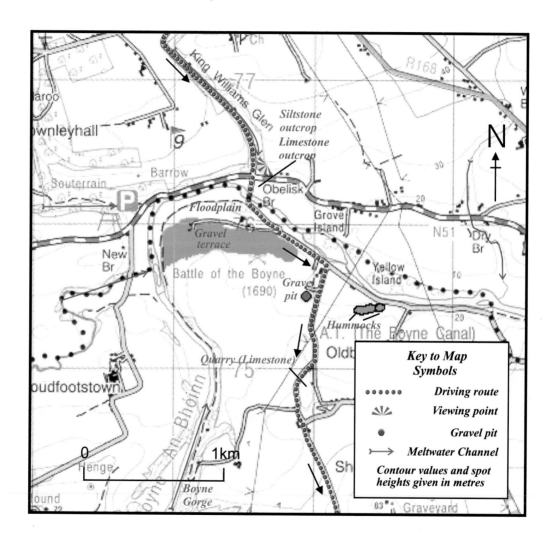

Site 3: Newgrange (NGR 3006 2727)

The great megalithic tomb at Newgrange is over 5,000 years old (older than the pyramids of Egypt). For three days around the winter solstice (the shortest day of the year) the rising sun casts a beam of light through a specially constructed box over the entrance, creeps up the passage-way and bathes the chamber in sunlight for twenty minutes.

Newgrange

The Brú na Bóinne interpretative centre at Newgrange has been built into the valley side. The sediments at this location are composed of glaciofluvial sands and gravels. The sands and gravels are exposed in a disused gravel pit 100 m east of the interpretative centre and are seen as well bedded pebble gravels interbedded with sand layers. The majority of the stones are limestone. A good view of the Boyne Gorge can be seen from the footbridge crossing towards Newgrange: while on this bridge we can visualise the huge amounts of water which would have careered down the valley at this point in deglacial times (the water level would have been several metres over our heads). This gives some idea of the volumes of water necessary if such huge amounts of gravels are to be deposited as are present on either side of the valley flank.

The view from Newgrange is quite spectacular and in a sense mystical, which reflects the fact that the tomb itself had an unworldly as well as worldly function during the Neolithic Period and later Brú na Bóinne was regarded by our Celtic ancestors as the home of the god Daghdha. The tumulus was built on a small, but prominent, hill which had been isolated from the land around it by meltwater erosion (in the main

Boyne Channel to the south and in the small meltwater channel which runs along the north side of the feature). To the south two terraces can be seen along with the present floodplain. Particularly noteworthy are the two deep feeder meltwater channels on the south side of the river at Roughgrange and Castlefin, which now house small streams. These, like King William's Glen, were cut by powerful flows of meltwater during the last deglaciation.

Driving between Newgrange and The Hill of Slane

Leaving Brú na Bóinne we pass by the deep channels at Roughgrange and Castlefin on our left hand side, with an impressive view of the terraces below the Newgrange tumulus on our right. Climbing the hill at Rossnaree we have a splendid view of Knowth tumulus through the trees on the right hand side of the road. The strategic positioning of the Knowth tumulus is also related to the glacial geology, the feature having been built on a high terrace on the side of the Boyne Gorge. Impressive views of the gorge can be seen driving past Rossnaree and from the viewing point close to the bridge south of Slane. Looking towards the Hill of Slane, five different land levels, related to the underlying geology, are clearly visible.

The highest of these is the Hill of Slane itself: a rock-cored feature which has been rounded by ice moulding. Below the hill a series of ice-moulded rock forms lie above Slane Village: these are explained in more detail in the description of the Hill of Slane below. Below these is a till plateau which contains some isolated rock outcrops: this is the main level which contains most of the houses on the Slane-

The terraces of the boyne viewed from Rosnaree.

Drogheda road and the village of Slane itself. The fourth level is one of well drained outwash gravels, which also includes a scattering of furze bushes. The lowest level is the modern river floodplain. Moving down through the levels is like travelling from the past to the present, with the oldest, rock-cored features at the top (having been moulded by ice during glacial maximum), a till level in the centre (again, reflecting glacial action), glaciofluvial sediments below this (from deglaciation and ice retreat) and the modern, most recent floodplain at the base.

When crossing Slane Bridge bedrock can be seen in the cliff on the northern side. The beds of rock have been folded (hence their zigzag, cross cutting nature) and planed at the top by ice. Hence the tops of the folds are missing and the beds look to have been stacked like playing cards against each other.

Site 4: Hill Of Slane (NGR 2960 2751)

The Hill of Slane site is associated with Saint Patrick, the 5th century patron saint of Ireland. Patrick kindled his Pascal Fire here in 433 A.D. This contravened the law that no fire should be lit on the eve of the feast of Bealtaine (literally Beal's Fire) before the king's fire had been lit and effectively announced the arrival of Christianity in Ireland. The Friary Church and college building at the summit date back to 1512 These had been preceded by an Early Christian monastery (founded by St Erc) and medieval abbey.

An impressive view can be gained from the viewpoint close to the Abbey reflecting the fact that this is a very prominent feature in the landscape. A fire lit on this hill top on a dark night would be seen over a very large part of the Boyne valley and beyond. The hill itself is cored by bedrock, shaped and rounded by ice and covered by a thin mantle of till. The ice-moulded rock features around Gallows Hill immediately south of the Hill of Slane are clearly seen, with craggy, bare sides and smooth crests protruding above the surrounding till plain. Looking east the Boyne Channel is almost invisible in the flat plain of east Meath. The only clue as to the whereabouts of the river itself is Knowth, which stands out just to the right of Platin Cement Works which again dominate the horizon. South of Platin itself, the Bellewstown ridge is clearly seen. To the northeast the drumlins of County Louth show a humpy landscape against the backdrop of the Mourne Mountains further to the northeast in County Down. Again, we may try to imagine how ice covered all of this landscape during the ice age.

Driving between Slane and Ardmulchan

The road from Slane passes Slane Castle, site of many large-scale outdoor concerts in recent years (the high curved valley flank forms a natural amphitheatre). Immediately past the castle on the north side of the road is Carrickdexter Hill, a dome of basalt mined extensively for road surfacing. On the east side of the hill a small stream has etched a channel and is underlain by a blanket of gravels, indicating that a wide river flowed through here during deglacial times. The flat area which borders this stream was completely taken up by the river which deposited the gravels. (The present stream has been incised since the Ice Age).

The Boyne River now parallels the road on the left and the area between the river and the road is underlain by till with some isolated, craggy rock outcrops. Limestone outcrops also occur in places along this road.

Turn left at Wicker's Cross Roads and cross the Boyne River, and left again immediately after Broadboyne Bridge. There is a gravel pit situated around the bend on the right hand side of the road. This pit is cut into the extensive gravel terrace which flanks the Boyne River on its southern side. The deposits consist of horizontal beds of gravel and sand, the gravels are generally cobble to pebble size. The stones are rounded due to the action of water. The sorted nature of these deposits also emphasises the importance of water during deglaciation in evolving the modern Boyne landscape. The gravels consist of limestone mostly, but many clasts of greenish Lower Palaeozoic sandstone are also present.

The road from the pit has been built in the centre of a small meltwater channel which is cut into limestone bedrock (the rock can be seen at the roadside). The channel flanks become more hummocky coming up to Stackallen Bridge where two isolated hummocks are present at Bridewell Bridge. These are kames composed of coarse boulder and cobble gravel.

Between Dollardstown and Ardmulchan the road traverses a flat plain mostly underlain by till. Turn into Ardmulchan from the road and park at the viewing point close to the church.

Site 5: Ardmulchan (NGR 2907 2702)

The church and adjoining bell tower at this picturesque site date from medieval times. Nearby Dunmoe Castle, though in ruins, is worthy of inspection, especially for its (still visible) vaulted ceilings on the lower storeys.

The site at Ardmulchan offers an excellent view of the components of a relict meltwater system. The sides of the valley are particularly striking with the south side having been eroded into a steep slope. The northern side also has various levels of erosion associated with meltwater. East of the church a small meltwater channel has been incised into the valley side, now housing a stream. This channel actually divides in two; the hillock in the centre having been deposited as an 'island' when the channel housed a river during deglaciation.

The view from Ardmulchan church, showing the floodplain and gravel terraces

This is the final stop on this tour with the town of Navan only 3 km away.

Touring Route 2: The Upper Boyne Valley (Navan-Trim-Navan).

Driving between Navan and Bective

Running south from Navan the road (R161) crosses a flat till plain as far as Balreask. This flat area underlain by till was deposited beneath the ice which crossed the area around 20,000 years ago. Passing Balsoon Demesne the road crosses a meltwater channel which has been incised into the underlying till by meltwater during deglaciation. Just past this meltwater channel, 7 km south of Navan, turn left towards Bective Abbey. This is the first stop on this tour.

Site 1: Bective Abbey (NGR 2859 2599)

Bective Abbey is a substantial remains of the second Cistercian monastery founded in Ireland in 1147. The remains are chiefly of a smaller 15th century abbey built on the site of the 12th and 13th century Gothic complex.

The Boyne Channel is quite wide at this point and has only one terrace on its northern side. The abbey is built on this terrace which provided an excellent level site, close to, but above the level of the river and its fertile floodplain and therefore dry and safe from floods when the river overflows its banks. The terrace is composed of glaciofluvial gravels which were laid down during deglaciation by the meltwater flowing through this part of the Boyne System from the Midlands. The modern floodplain is relatively wide close

The floodplain at Bective with the abbey to the left of the photo

to the Abbey and is generally sandy in texture, reflected in its well drained appearance. On the southern side of the river a steep escarpment has formed where the river has cut into the bedrock which is quite close to the surface at this point. In fact, on the southern side of Bective Bridge, 200 m from the road a steep cliff has been cut into a well bedded limestone outcrop. Behind this outcrop much of the area around Balsoon and Balgeeth is dominated by thick glaciofluvial gravels and sands which were deposited at the margin of the ice as it retreated across the area during deglaciation.

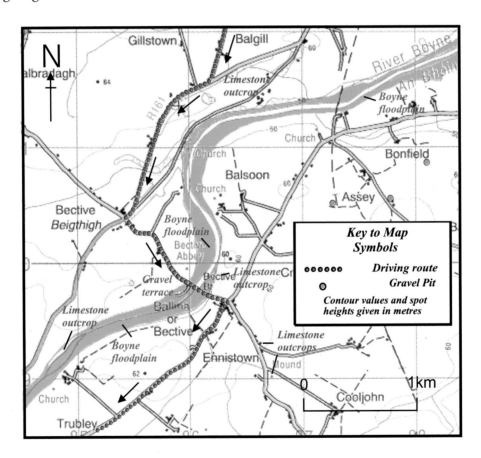

Driving between Bective and the Trim Esker

Turn right in Bective Village and follow the road as far as Scurlockstown. The road to Scurlockstown traverses a till plain (the same plain as flanking the Navan-Bective road, the tills of this plain have been incised by the River Boyne since they were originally deposited). This entire area is underlain by Carboniferous limestone bedrock and relatively thick till deposits. Upon reaching Scurlockstown a gorse covered feature is visible to the west of the cross-roads. Having turned right on to the main road, turn left at Scurlockstown House and then left again at Iffernock the road actually follows this feature southwards. The feature itself is the Trim Esker.

Site 2: Trim Esker (NGR 2858 2525)

Nearby Trim is the site of the largest Norman Castle in Ireland. Built in 1173 by Hugh de Lacy, it has scarcely been modified since it was completed in the 13th century. Other landmarks in Trim include St. Mary's Abbey (12th century), St. Patrick's Cathedral (15th century), the Yellow Steeple (14th century) and the Newtown complex of Cathedral, church and monasteries. This was one of the most important medieval settlements in Ireland with, in addition to the castle, seven monasteries and three hospitals. Access was by river and road. Eskers provided excellent natural dry foundations for roads and many ancient routes followed them. The esker we are about to follow is one such and as we can drive along this road the full length of the esker avoiding the low wet ground on either side until we reach the high ground at Moynalvy, within ten kilometres of the great east - west esker route across Ireland which followed the great Eiscir Riada.

The esker is 14.5 km long and is one of the finest examples in Ireland. Initially the road follows along the east side of the feature (some small gravel scars are visible to the west of the road) but then rises up onto the crest. You are now on top of the esker. This gravel ridge was deposited by a river flowing through a tunnel beneath the ice sheet. Part of the esker was laid down as the gravel bed of this river and more of it was deposited at the mouth of the tunnel in a lake that was dammed between the edge of the ice sheet and the higher ground to the southeast.. When the ice melted at the end of glaciation the esker was left standing above the surrounding landscape. The road falls down again to the left of the feature after about 2km and follows alongside it as far as the Trim Esker gravel pit (which is still in operation).

While approaching the pit it will be noticed that the land on our left is very hummocky. These hummocks are kame features which have been deposited in crevasses in the ice and let down on the

The Trim Esker just south of Galtrim.

underlying till (see section on The Record of Meltwater during deglaciation).

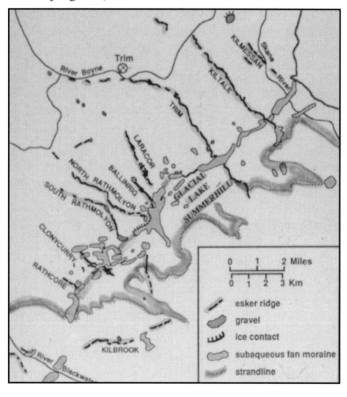

The pit is cut into the centre of the esker and offers views of its structures across its lateral and longitudinal planes, thus allowing us to examine in some detail how exactly the esker was deposited. The ridge is 16 m - 18 m high at this point, and is seen to be composed of coarse gravels (commonly cobble or boulder size) which are relatively well sorted. This indicates that they were deposited by running water which was flowing at a very high rate. Try to visualise the power of such a high flow regime by imagining how much fast flowing water is needed to transport gravels of that size.

Driving between the Trim Esker and Basketstown

Leave the pit and travel south, turning right just after Galtrim Church. At the road junction here a kame was modified by the early Normans to make a Moat. The esker feature is now at right-angles to the road. Parallel to the road on the southern side is a well-drained ridge. This is a delta moraine (see next site). The esker actually overtops this ridge here at Galtrim Crossroads: this is the only reported site in the world where an esker crosses a moraine.

The Trim Esker approaching Galtrim. Taken from the moraine

The flat area adjoining the Trim Esker at Galtrim.

Site 3: Basketstown (NGR 2856 2516)

Nearby, at Laracor, Stella's Cottage is the former home of Esther Johnson, companion to Dean Swift, author of Gulliver's Travels. The cottage is now in ruins but only a short trip from Basketstown.

The pit at Basketstown is cut into a feature which is composed of discontinuous ridges of sand and gravel, known as the Galtrim Moraine. These were deposited as ice-contact fans or deltas into Glacial Lake Summerhill. The ice was to the north: meltwater was ponded against the Summerhill Escarpment to the south creating an irregularly-shaped lake. The exposure in this pit reveals beds of sand and gravel dipping to the east, southeast and south. The gravels are generally clean and well-washed, and very well-sorted. Some disturbed beds indicate that the sediment pile was pushed by an active, oscillating ice margin while the gravels were being deposited.

Driving between Basketstown and Tara

Turning west along the road from Basketstown and passing Ginnets House some small elongate ridges come into view. These are small moraines deposited at the ice margin as it retreated across the area, some were deposited at the same time (and along the same ice margin) as the Basketstown Ridge. Turning left at Dangan a high esker is seen on the right hand side of the road. This is oriented northwest to southeast and therefore parallels the Trim Esker; this indicates that as the ice covered this area it contained a series of tunnels in its base which drained meltwater from the ice. As there are twelve eskers in the area at least twelve large tunnels existed. The road then crosses a till plain between here and Summerhill. The Summerhill escarpment now dominates the horizon south of the town. The shale bedrock, of Carboniferous (Namurian) age, making up this feature can clearly be seen in the disused quarry 500 m west of the village cross-roads. The escarpment formed the southern shore of a lake into which the Basketstown Delta was deposited (imagine that the village was totally submerged in water at that time). Take the first right at Summerhill Village towards Rathmolyon.

The road between these two villages crosses a flat till plain before rising up over a hummocky ridge composed of sands and gravels. This ridge is also a moraine, deposited at the ice margin at the same time as the Basketstown Delta. Many of the hollows between the hummocks are badly drained kettle holes. The furze covered feature which can be seen on the north of the road is an esker which feeds into the hummocky moraine feature. This is a further indication of the tunnels under the ice, through which water flowed and fed sand and gravel to the moraine.

Turning northwards at Rathmolyon the road passes another esker ridge. Between here and Laracor the road again crosses the till plain which forms the flat land between the hummocks and esker features. At Laracor yet another northwest-southeast oriented esker occurs, this is best seen from the top of Bray Hill where the esker actually splits into two ridges. Bray Hill is cored by limestone bedrock which has been polished by the action of ice during the last glaciation.

Pass by the Trim Esker at Scurlockstown and take the R154 road southeastwards. The esker is clearly visible to the west paralleling the road. At Pike Corner turn left towards Kilmessan. The road continually crosses a till plain, the undulatory nature of which is best seen around Pike Corner where the large fields give a good view of the monotonous nature of the feature. Just before Kilmessan Village a small, disused gravel pit is visible on the northwest of the road; this has been dug into a kame. An impressive view of the Hill of Tara, which occurs straight ahead, is seen here.

Through the village we pass over the alluvial flat of the Skane River. Turn right at Ringlestown after passing Kilmessan GAA Pitch and travel towards the hill summit. Turning left at the top, you can park in the car park at Tara itself.

Site 4: Hill of Tara (NGR 2920 2597)

The Hill of Tara was the Seat of the High Kings of Ireland and is source to many of the Great Legends. The site has been an important one since the Neolithic (Stone Age) when a passage tomb was built. It had its heyday in the third century A.D. following the reign of King Cormac Mac Airt.

The hill is cored by limestone bedrock which was streamlined by ice during the ice age. The bedrock once outcropped on the southern side of the hill but has since been removed by small-scale quarrying, the scars of which can still be seen. The view from the hill is quite spectacular, showing the entire Boyne Valley and a very large part of the east midlands. The region dominated by the Hill of Tara covers some of the richest farm land in Ireland. It is an area

The Hill of Tara

underlain by a thick covering of till and glacial sands and gravels. The high hills of Slieve na Calliagh and Lloyd Hill can be seen to the northwest, the Mourne Mountains to the northeast, the Wicklow Mountains to the southeast and Slieve Bloom (in the distance) to the southwest. Skryne Hill to the east is the next stop.

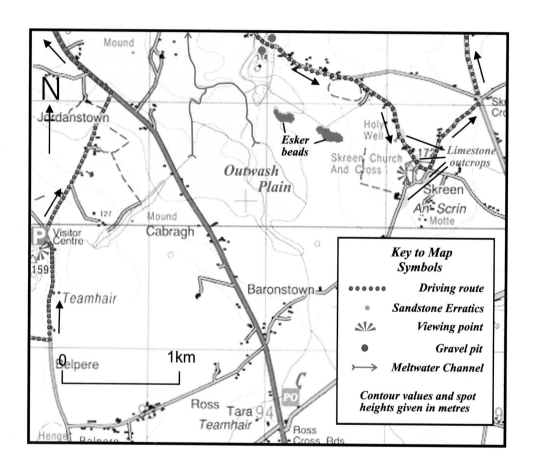

Driving between Tara and Skryne

Leaving Tara Hill and turning back towards Navan on the N3 we travel over the wide, alluvium floored channel tributary stream to the Boyne. This channel conducted water towards the Boyne during the last deglaciation and is now flanked by sands and gravels which were deposited at that time. Turning right at Garlow Cross and looking back at Tara it can be seen that the high hill is enveloped by a lower, flat-topped ridge which forms the southern flank of the channel we have just crossed. This is actually a moraine which was deposited by ice pushing up against the bedrock of the Hill of Tara.

Taking the road to the right at the fork for Skryne Hill, some pronounced rounded hillocks separated by channels are present on either side of the road. These hillocks are composed of gravel and were deposited by meltwater during deglaciation. Their form was the accentuated by meltwater flowing between them, causing the channels and the associated steep sides to the features. The road rises towards Skryne Hill with bedrock cropping out at the top of the hill. A short esker ridge can be seen at the base of the hill between here and the Hill of Tara.

Site 5: Skryne Hill (NGR 2952 2605)

Skryne was an early Christian monastery, and is called after the Shrine of Saint Columcille's relics. The 15th century holy well is dedicated to St. Columcille. The moat (motte) of De Phirpo, the first baron of Skryne, can be seen from the hill, as well as the castle that replaced it.

Skryne Hill, composed of shaley Carboniferous limestone, emerges through the flat and well-drained glaciofluvial sands and gravels that extend east from the foot of Tara Hill. These gravels comprise the outwash plain which was deposited in front of the ice as it stood between the two hills during deglaciation. The plain is dissected by a number of channels which eventually link up with the channels east of Garlow

Cross. On the northern side of the base of the hill two elongated hummocks are present. These are two beads of an esker which were deposited (earlier than the outwash gravels) under the ice which filled the area between the two hills. It is difficult to see rock outcrop on the top of Skryne Hill today as much of the area has been landscaped.

Driving between Skryne through Kentstown to Navan

From Skryne take the road northwards through Skryne Cross-roads to Cusackstown where the road to the left should be followed. Here, at Cusackstown, the road follows the base of a network of meltwater channels. Drive onto the next cross-roads and turn right into Kentstown along the northern edge of the Nanny Valley. This deep valley was again cut by meltwater during deglaciation and carried much of the Boyne water while the ice sheet stood just north of here. The road from Kentstown back to Navan follows a till plain with Brownstown Hill, which is rock-cored, dominating the landscape on the northern side of the road.

Touring Route 3: Western County Meath (Navan-Athboy-Oldcastle).

Driving between Navan and Tullaghanstown

Take the Athboy road from Navan. Before crossing the railway bridge past Navan Hospital a high hill looms over the north side of the road. This is Navan Moat, an early Norman fortified site. The moat, or motte, is built on a moraine which was deposited at the ice front when it stabilised at Navan for a short period during the last deglacial period. The Normans were adept at modifying hills such as this to provide a palisaded hilltop defensive site pending the construction of a castle. The hill itself is composed of layers of till and sorted gravels. The flat area west of the moat which extends for several kilometres west of Navan Town is a flat till plain. Tara Mines can be seen to the north of the railway crossing. Here the limestone bedrock beneath the till is intensely faulted and folded and has resulted in the mineralisation of lead and zinc along many of the major joints. The limestone is overlain by several metres of the till which comprises the till plain. The till gives rise to thick topsoils which provide almost perfect conditions for pastoral farming. Past Halltown Cross-roads the flat area is underlain by marl deposits which were deposited into a temporary glacial lake.

Site 1: Tullaghanstown Bog (NGR 2787 2655)

This bog covers an area of about 5 square kilometres and in some places is over 10 m deep. It is an excellent example of a Midland raised bog, taking the form of a peat-filled hollow or depression in which the surface of the peat rises from the margins to the centre forming a dome, thus it is "raised". Peat formation began almost immediately following the last glaciation about 10,000 years ago.

Tullaghanstown Bog formed here in a wide flat basin which had held a glacial lake as the ice sheets melted and which was floored by glaciolacustrine clays. In the early postglacial period there would have been a shallow lake here. As the vegetation (aquatic plants in the lake water and semi aquatics near the shore) died and accumulated in the basin, it began to form peat. This decreased water depth and resulted in the gradual encroachment of

Tullaghanstown Bog.

vegetation into the lake and a fen was established As the margins of the fen became invaded by reedswamp plants and bulrushes, and as other submerged plants established themselves in shallow waters, the accumulating vegetable debris eventually consolidated into fen peat, which continued its build up as time went on. As the peat further accumulated and the bog rose above the surrounding area above the influence of the mineral soil the vegetation changed and it became a raised bog with a very different vegetative cover dominated by sphagnum moss. Peat in an undisturbed bog is composed more than 90% of water. The rest is dead vegetative matter. Thus a bog contains less solid matter and more water than milk, yet it is possible to walk on it. On close inspection branches, twigs, leaves and moss can be clearly seen in the peat and it is these that tell us how the bog formed. Many of the fields along the road just past the main peat area were once part of the bog also, but at some of these locations the peat has been largely removed for fuel over the last two centuries.

Driving between Tullaghanstown Bog and the Hill of Ward

Past the bog and as far as the Hill of Ward the road crosses a till plain. Around Rathmore, near the site of the old church, the land is very well drained as the underlying till is especially gravelly, and water can percolate through it with ease.

Site 2: Hill of Ward (NGR 2735 2644)

Situated on the summit of the Hill of Ward (Tlachta) is an Iron Age fort which was, according to legend, one of the four residences of the High Kings of Ireland..

The Hill of Ward is cored by limestone bedrock which is very close to the surface at its summit. The bedrock has been eroded and shaped into a dome-shaped hill by the movement of ice from northwest to southeast during the last glaciation. At the northwest side of the cross-roads close to the summit there exists an old, disused quarry cut into the limestone. The quarry exposes folded beds of limestone which have been sheared at the top by ice, truncating the folds. On the sides of the hill a thin covering of lodgement till has been deposited on the bedrock. The view from the top of the hill shows the plain of central Meath with sporadic high hills, such as Tara to the east, protruding above the till plain. To the west the bogs of Westmeath can be seen in the distance.

Driving between the Hill of Ward and Lough Bane

From Athboy take the road northwest towards Clonmellon. The road parallels the Athboy River and crosses what is mostly a till plain, but the hummocky area around Martinstown is a collection of moraine deposits. These accumulated at the ice margin while it was retreating northwards at the end of glaciation. Several hummocks are also present around Drewstown. These are kames interspersed with some kettle holes (White Lough is situated in such a depression). Turning left at Johnsbrook Cross-roads into Clonmellon, it can be seen that the area close to the road gets increasingly hummocky. These hummocks are mostly kames, again interspersed with deep kettle holes. Through Clonmellon take the road west as far as Killallon Village. The hummocks around this locality are all kames which formed in or on top of the ice close to its margin and were subsequently let down on the substrate as the ice melted. This area is one of the best examples of a kame and kettle topography in the country and extends well into County Westmeath. Passing through Herbertstown Cross-roads the hummocks get bigger (up to 30m high) and are arranged in a more linear fashion. These features are actually moraines which mark the former position of the ice margin as the ice retreated towards the west across this area.

At Cross Keys turn left. The road dips and passes a deep channel. This is a meltwater channel which was cut by water escaping from a lake which covered the area north of here during deglaciation. Passing westwards to Skerry Cross-roads, Lough Bane can be seen. Turn left and park on the eastern shore of the lake.

Site 3: Lough Bane (NGR 2557 2711)

Lough Bane is situated in an area of exceptional natural beauty. The Seven Wonders of Fore provide an interesting nature trail close by, based on ordinary things you can find in the valley (their ordinariness probably strengthens their reputation). The wonders include water that flows uphill and wood that will not burn.

Lough Bane is situated between two high escarpments which are made up of chert rock. Like Lough Lene, Lough Derravaragh, Lough Owel and many other smaller lakes in this area, it was gouged out of the broad ridge of limestone and chert running southwest from Slieve na Calliagh by ice flowing southeastwards from the north midlands. These lakes are elongate and aligned northwest - southeast reflecting the flow of ice and, although smaller, might be compared to the finger lakes of New York State. Chert is a hard material composed of microcrystalline quartz or opaline

Cherty crag beside Lough Bane

Lough Bane with its surrounding cliffed hills

silica and usually occurs as nodules or beds in limestone. In the area of Lough Bane the chert bands are several metres thick, resulting in high cliffs of really resistant material. These are actually the sides of a glacially scoured valley, with Lough Bane covering its floor (the smaller lake, Lough Glass, occurs to the southeast of Lough Bane). This valley is not a typical U-shaped valley, such as Glendalough or Glenmacnass in Wicklow, but is still primarily the result of glacial action: the valley having been over-deepened by the ice. On its eastern side the lake is separated from the much smaller Lough Glass by a small gravel moraine feature, comprised of two small hummocks. This effectively 'dams' the lake on its eastern flank. Try to imagine a large glacier filling the valley and depositing the moraine separating the two lakes. You can examine the hard chert rock by walking up to the cliffs on the southern side but take care, the scree which has collected at the base of the cliffs is very loose. The beds can be seen from the road where the rocks themselves crop out.

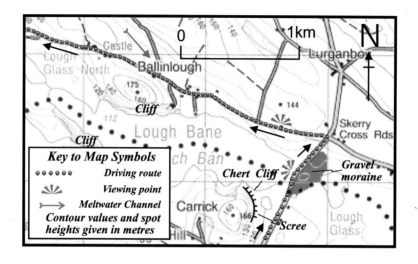

Driving between Lough Bane and Slieve na Calliagh

Turning west at Skerry Cross roads we pass the high hill of Seafin and its associated ridges which are again composed of chert, hence the craggy sides and frequent occurrence of outcropping bedrock (generally furze covered). Turning right at Ballanny Cross-roads the landscape is very hummocky and well drained. This area is underlain by well-sorted gravels and sands. Driving for 2 km through this landscape gives some idea of the huge volumes of gravels in this area. You can stop at the gravel pit at Murrens (there are two working pits, back to back). Permission must be sought to look at the gravels. The pit covers almost 1 square kilometre.

The gravels here are unusual in their coarseness, with many of the stones cobble or boulder size. All of these clasts, though large, are still quite well rounded indicating that they were transported by running water. You will cross a flat area which is underlain by silts and sands. These are the fine sediments that were deposited around the edge of a glacial lake during deglaciation. The high ridge of Slieve na Calliagh is visible ahead of you. Take the road along the south side of the ridge and drive up to the car park at the entrance to the Loughcrew Passage Graves. On the way up, keep an eye on the view to the south over the hummocky area. Many of the hummocks are moraines which were deposited along the ice margin.

Roche moutonnée on Slieve na Calliagh

Site 4: Slieve na Calliagh (NGR 2577 2772)

Slieve na Calliagh itself means the Mountain of the Hag. The Loughcrew Megalithic Tombs have decorated stones in the same pattern as Newgrange, and the tombs have an astronomical function which is much more complicated than the Brú na Bóinne complex. The nearby Loughcrew Demesne is the birthplace of Saint Oliver Plunkett and the family church is still standing.

Walk up to Carnbane West from the car park (*i.e.* the ridge to the west). The ribbed features visible on the ground are cultivation ridges on which crops were once grown up to and during the last century. The ridges were formed using a spade. On top of the hill bedrock crops out: this rock is of Lower Palaeozoic age. The passage of ice across it during the last glaciation smoothed the hilltop and plucked southern side (note the jagged southern side).

Sandstone Erratic on the crest of Slieve na Calliagh

These small outcrops are therefore roche moutonnée forms. Between Carnbane West and Patrickstown (the westernmost peak), the bedrock has been smoothed by ice into streamlined forms, again a type of roche moutonnée as the features are steeper on their southern, or down ice, side. The most striking feature on the top of this first hill is the presence of a large boulder. This is a sandstone erratic which has been carried to the top of the ridge, by ice during the last glaciation, from its source northwest of Slieve na Calliagh. Boulders of the same sandstone can be found strewn across the entire ridge crest. In fact, many of the stones comprising the Loughcrew Tombs themselves are of this sandstone, and have obviously been picked up from their resting place across the ridge during the construction of the tombs.

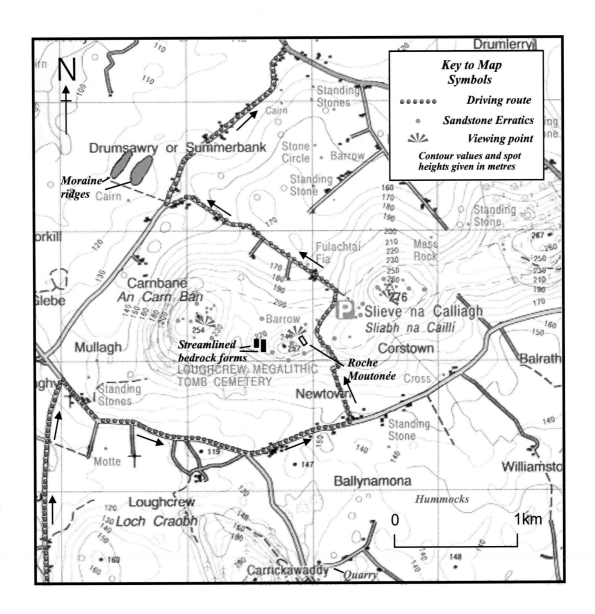

Key to Map Symbols

••••••	Driving route
•	Sandstone Erratics
⚜	Viewing point

Contour values and spot heights given in metres

Drumlerryl

Drumsawry or Summerbank

Moraine ridges

Cairn

Cairn

Standing Stones

Stone Circle

Barrow

Standing Stone

Standing Stone

orkill

Fulachtaí Fía

Mass Rock

267

Carnbane
An Carn Bán

276

Slieve na Calliagh
Sliabh na Cailli

Glebe

254

Barrow

Streamlined bedrock forms

257

Roche Moutonée

Corstown

Balrath

Mullagh

LOUGHCREW MEGALITHIC
TOMB CEMETERY

Newtov

Cross

Standing Stones

Standing Stone

Williamst

Motte

119

147

Ballynamona

Hummocks

148

Loughcrew
Loch Craobh

0   1km

163

160

Carrickawaddy   *Quarry*

It is not surprising that our distant ancestors chose this site as one of their most important religious and astronomical centres. The view from the top of the ridge is quite spectacular. To the north the drumlin region is clearly visible, with Lough Sheelin in the distance. Lough Ramor cannot be seen from this location but its whereabouts can be gauged by finding the Blackwater Valley to the north. South of the ridge feature the linear moraines of the Diamor area can be seen to the east of the high, wooded ridges of Loughcrew Demesne. Looking west, in the near distance the Murrens Gravel complex is visible, as well as the high peaks at Fore and those further west. It is said that sixteen counties are visible from Slieve na Calliagh on a very clear day. You should be able to make out at least half of these!!

Driving between Slieve na Calliagh and Oldcastle

You should descend the ridge on the northern side. Where the road from Slieve na Calliagh meets the road on the northern side of the ridge, in the field across the road two fine examples of small moraines can be seen. These were deposited at the ice margin as the ice retreated northwards away from the ridge. The moundy topography in the field to the right (and further north) is also composed of haphazard agglomerations of morainic material. Between here and Oldcastle the land is very hummocky. These hummocks are also mounds of morainic material deposited by the ice on the northern side of Slieve na Calliagh during the retreat. On the southern side of the road some erratics can still be seen in the fields, standing out on the green pastures. One peaty area is particularly badly drained.

The composition of these moraines can be seen clearly in the road cutting (4m high) just south of Millbrook Cross-roads. The material in this cutting is unsorted with many angular boulders of limestone protruding. These unsorted agglomerations are typical of morainic deposits, with a sandy/silty matrix and very angular stones.

Touring Route 4: North Meath (Oldcastle-Kingscourt-Navan).

Driving between Oldcastle and Castlekeeran

Leaving Oldcastle on the R154 the road crosses a well-drained, hummocky landscape, again containing moraines comprised of stony material. The mounds of debris on the northern side of the Slieve na Calliagh ridge are clearly visible, reminding us that the ice deposited thousands of tonnes of material against the ridge during its retreat. The outcropping bedrock along the roadside on the top of the ridge gives a good insight into the structure of the rock. Stay on the R154 as far as Crossakeel. The land between the Slieve na Calliagh ridge and Crossakeel is underlain by relatively thick, silty to clayey till. The fine-grained texture results from the grinding down of the very fine-grained stones by the ice to form the till. At Crossakeel Village an impressive view is had of the lowland west of here. The ridge at Crossakeel itself is composed of bedrock of the same age as Slieve na Calliagh.

Between Crossakeel and Ballally Cross-roads the land is underlain by clayey till which is not very thick, hence the frequent outcropping of bedrock along the route. Turning right at Ballally, the ridge on the right of the road covered in furze is a moraine. Around Keerans Cross-roads (where we turn right) it can be noticed that the land is much more hummocky, as well as being much better drained. This is due to the fact that the area is underlain by well-sorted sands and gravels.

Site 1: Castlekeeran Holy Well and High Crosses
(NGR 2687 2771 and 2691 2773)

The High Crosses at Castlekeeran are older than those at Kells: the graveyard there also contains an early Christian grave slab and an excellent example of a decorated Ogham Stone. Ogham is the ancient Celtic script generally used on commemorative stones. It was gradually replaced by Latin-based letters in the seventh century but continued in use until the early middle ages. The nearby Holy Well was, according to legend, formed at St. Kieran's command. Several pools there have supposed healing powers.

The holy well at Castlekeeran provides an interesting stop at both the geological and the curiosity level. The bedrock outcropping here is of Carboniferous limestone which has been karstified. The limestone at the well is very pure which means that it is rich in calcium carbonate and is easily dissolved by mildly acidic rainwater. This solution produces grooves and channels in the bedrock such as we see here and leads to the formation of caves and streams which disappear underground and reappear. No direct evidence for such caves has been found at this site, but we can be fairly sure that the water present in the wells is indicative of a network of small caverns which were carved by solution in the underlying rock. The solution forms seen here all formed after glacial ice had melted.

Outcropping limestone bedrock at Castlekeeran Holy Well

The nearby high crosses are built on a well drained terrace which was the last gravel layer deposited at the end of deglaciation by the River Blackwater, before it was lowered to its present channel. Looking northwestwards up the valley the landscape is dominated by low, hummocky ridges which are all composed of gravel too. The structure of these gravels can be seen clearly in Harton's Pit near Carnaross (visible from the main N3 road). Looking towards Carnaross from the crosses a gravel terrace can also be seen on the north side of the river.

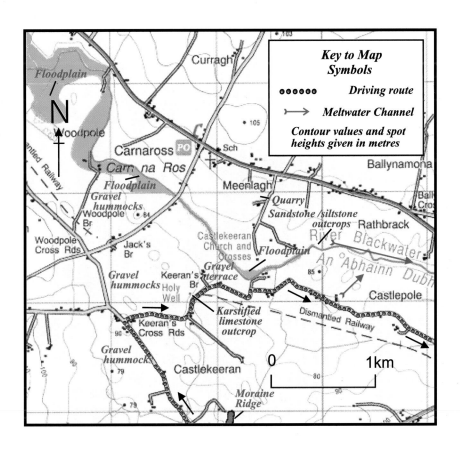

Driving between Castlekeeran and Lloyd Hill

The road follows alongside the Blackwater River which is flanked by valley sides composed of thin till over bedrock. The gravel terraces are absent here as the deglacial Blackwater Valley was constrained by these rock-cored flanks and has etched a deeper channel here than elsewhere along its course (this part of the river was eroding rather than depositing). Lloyd Hill is also a bedrock-cored ridge with a thin mantle of till. The tower on the hill provides an excellent view of the surrounding countryside; you can access this tower from the car park beside it.

Site 2: Lloyd Hill (NGR 2724 2765)

The tower at the top of this hill was built in 1791 under the direction of the first Earl of Bective. The top of the tower is accessible by a spiral stone staircase, from which a magnificent view of the surrounding countryside is had.

The hill is composed of Lower Palaeozoic age bedrock with a thin veneer of till. The northern side has been moulded by ice which shows clearly the direction of ice flow around the ridge from northwest to southeast.

Immediately around the hill much of the outcrop is hummocky. Other bedrock bumps have been veneered with a thin sheet of till. Thus the hummocky topography here is bedrock controlled. To the immediate south of the hill a long, linear ridge running northwest - southeast and covered with gorse bushes is seen. This is the Sherry Esker. Looking north, the Blackwater flows from west to east at the foot of Lloyd Hill. West of the ridge the sides of the Blackwater Channel become quite steep and the channel has clearly been cut by meltwater (this is east of Castlekeeran, Stop 1). North of the town of Kells the well drained hummocks of gravel are clearly seen. Bedrock comes close to the surface beneath the town itself and beneath the wooded area of Headfort Demesne. Headfort Estate is curious as the graveyard is built on a number of small alluvial islands which have been deposited in the centre of the Blackwater River.

Driving between Lloyd Hill and Kingscourt

The drive between Kells and Kingscourt is quite a long one but passes through some of the most scenic areas of the Boyne Valley and its surrounds. Between Kells and Moynalty the land is composed of small, gently undulating hillocks which are interspersed with poorly drained hollows. These hummocks are formed of outwash gravels. Around Moynalty Village, the hillocks themselves are more pronounced, having been dissected and their heights accentuated by rivers flowing around them at the end of the ice age.

Between Moynalty and Ervey the land is dominated by drumlins and interdrumlin hollows. The only other major landform element is the Carrickspringan Escarpment, its rocky crags having been plucked by glaciers and its summit having been polished by the ice. The ridge is composed of very resistant impure sandstones (greywacke) of Lower Palaeozoic age. Just past Ervey Cross-roads the road is flanked on either side by high, steep slopes as it follows the base of a meltwater channel. This is cut into till. Between here and Kingscourt drumlins again dominate the landscape.

Meltwater channel at Ervey

Site 3: Kingscourt (NGR 2786 2952)

The town of Kingscourt is built on the west side of a deep valley. This valley dates back to the Permian Era but the most striking aspect of the view from the town (the best viewing points are on the southern side of the town) are the hundreds of drumlins clustered on the lowland between here and the Mourne Mountains. The drumlins are composed of till and are oriented northwest-southeast. The base of the valley is floored by smaller, well drained hummocks of sand and gravel which are testament to the fact that the channel was used by meltwater at the end of deglaciation. The valley itself was probably over-deepened by the ice during glaciation.

Drumlins near Kingscourt

Driving between Kingscourt and Nobber

The road from Kingscourt drops down into the valley along its western side, dropping among the drumlins which flank it. As the road crosses the railway you are at the lowest point of the valley, now quite flat and housing a river floodplain. Rising and travelling towards Nobber we are again among drumlins with the valley to the right (the village of Kilmainhamwood is situated at the base of the valley and is surrounded by several gravel pits cut into the gravels which were laid down in the valley by glacial meltwater). Whitewood and Newcastle Loughs are dammed by these meltwater gravel hummocks and the valley sides.

Site 4: Nobber (NGR 2817 2867)

Nobber is the birthplace of the last of the Irish Bards, Turlough O'Carolan, who was born in 1670. He traversed the northern half of Ireland as a travelling bard, and wrote more than 200 pieces of music. An Irish music festival is held in his honour at Nobber each summer.

One of the best views of the drumlins in the area occurs just north of Nobber Village where the road bends around to the right. West of the village, close to the River Dee, some hummocks can be seen. These are moraines. The first five kilometres of the road between Nobber Village and Castletown is quite like a roller coaster as it rises up and down over the humpbacked drumlins.

Driving between Nobber and Demailstown

Driving south from Nobber drumlins dominate the landscape. Passing Cross Guns Pub and Mullens Cross-roads, the drumlins die out and are replaced by smaller, more haphazard, 5m-6m high hummocks which are comprised of sorted gravel. These are exposed in the road cutting at Darby's Cross-roads. The gravels here record the huge amounts of meltwater that existed in this area flowing from the drumlin region during deglaciation. Turn left at Wilkinstown and then right towards Demailstown. A deep valley is visible on the left hand side after 2 km or so. Stop at the T-junction with the minor road towards Kilberry; there is a wide verge here which facilitates parking.

Site 5: Demailstown (NGR 2874 2750)

Demailstown is only three miles from Teltown, site of one of the four royal palaces of Ireland in ancient times. It was also the location of the Tailteann Games, an annual gathering of sport similar to the Olympics of ancient Greece. The games were held on the first of August from the 15th century B.C. to as late as the 12th century A.D.

The view east at Demailstown across the valley is quite interesting and records the complex developmental history of the valley. The highest ridges are bedrock cored with a thin covering of till in some places; furze bushes often indicate areas where rock is

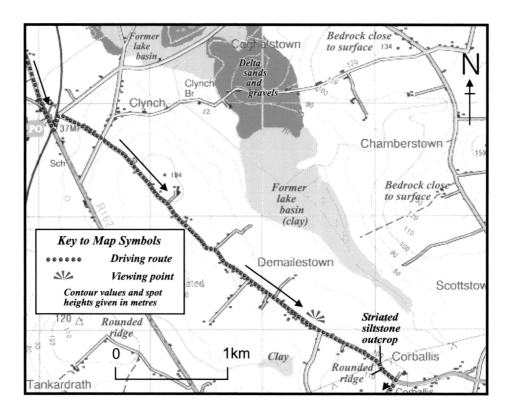

outcropping. On the north side of the bedrock ridge (Mullagha Hill) directly opposite a flat-topped feature is seen, with houses built across its crest. This flat-topped feature is a delta and is composed of bedded sands and gravels. At the end of deglaciation ice had so reduced in thickness that only a tongue of ice covered the valley floor, with its front retreating towards the north. The ice stood still at the northern side of the valley and a large lake formed from the meltwater, filling the valley up to between the 80 and 90 metre contour. Meltwater rivers flowing off the ice at the northern side of the valley deposited sorted sands and gravels as a delta: then as the ice retreated further north the meltwater filling the valley drained away northwards *via* the meltwater channel at Clynch Bridge. The delta was then left standing as it is today, a relict feature of sands and gravels. The floor of the valley at Demailstown is covered in poorly drained glaciolacustrine silts and clays which were deposited while the lake was in existence.

Nearby, just inside the field on the west side of Corballis Cross-roads, there is an old quarry. The siltstone rock cropping out at the quarry has been clearly striated along a west-east plane. Measuring the striae provides valuable information about ice flow over the area during the last glaciation.

Driving between Demailstown and Simonstown

Between Kilberry and Navan the ground is covered with a veneer of till, hence the well developed, fertile valleys with thick topsoils. Crossing the top of Proudstown Hill the bedrock can be seen cropping out at the roadside. The outwash plain at Simonstown is best seen at the base of Proudstown Hill. Looking west, the flat surface of the plain can be seen to terminate in a series of small hummocks on the western horizon. This is where the ice margin stood at the time of deposition of the outwash gravels. The extensive Kilsaran Gravel Pit can be seen and can be accessed by turning right at the lane beside the Navan Tyre Centre. The gravels in the Kilsaran Pit are organised in extensive horizontal layers which are sheets of sands and gravels which were deposited on top of each other by the meltwater rivers. Please ask permission at the entrance to the concrete works if you wish to gain access to the pit. This concludes the fourth geological tour within one kilometre of Navan.

The Last Great Ice Age.

What might we see if we imagine the Ice Age? A barren landscape, devoid of life? Hundreds of thousands of tonnes of dead, inert ice and snow? In reality, the ice age was a period of intense activity in our surrounding natural environment. A somewhat strange but often ignored fact is, that if we take a **global** view on the Earth's climate we are actually living in an Ice Age today, as huge volumes of the Earth's water are frozen in ice sheets, particularly in Antarctica and Greenland. It was not until the mid nineteenth century that scientists realised that in the past, the global temperature cooled further and ice sheets extended to cover large areas; with conditions then warming again to force the ice sheets to reduce to their present size. Since then studies on the landforms and sediments deposited by these glaciers have given great insight into the scale and timing of past glaciations, often in areas which are unglaciated today.

This most recent period of geological time is called the Quaternary. Generally it is taken to cover the last 1.65 million years, right up to the present day. It is subdivided into two epochs which are the Pleistocene (1.65 million to 10,000 years ago) and the Holocene (10,000 years ago to the present). The Holocene, in Ireland, is the postglacial period. The Quaternary Period has seen remarkable changes in world climate. During this time much of human evolution has taken place.

(Colman Gallagher)

Glacier tongue in Alaska

The Earth itself is 4,600 million years old. Throughout the 4,600 million years the surface temperature of the Earth has undergone considerable fluctuations, varying from intensely hot conditions to severely cold. Evidence from deep sea drilling suggests that the current cold period began about 45 million years ago, when western Europe's climate was very warm and subtropical. Since then temperatures lowered continually until ice began to develop in the Polar Regions about 25 million years ago. At the start of the Quaternary Period western European temperatures were as they are today; cool and temperate. At that time the Polar ice caps and Greenland ice cap were about the same size as they are now.

Since then the extent of the ice caps has fluctuated greatly, with a series of sudden temperature changes affecting global climate. The boundaries of the ice masses have moved back and forth and extended well into the mid-latitudes at times. During some of the colder periods Ireland was engulfed by glacial ice as part of an ice sheet that extended across northwest Europe from northern Scandinavia to southwest Ireland. These colder stages (ice ages to us in Ireland, as we were inundated with ice) are called glacials and the warmer stages are termed interglacials.

It was these extensions of ice into our latitudes that were responsible for much of the shaping of our landscape and for depositing much of the material above solid rock in this country. This is due partly to the way in which the ice broke up and ground down much of the bedrock over which it moved (we can imagine the amount of erosive, destructive power a few hundred metres of moving ice would have had on the rocks and other sediments below it), and also to the way in which the millions of tonnes of debris so gathered by the ice was both spread out under the ice and released from the ice as it finally melted.

Quaternary sediments differ from earlier sediments in that they are generally unconsolidated or unlithified. The country's solid geology is much older. In general, Late Quaternary sediments are thousands of years old whereas older, solid rock sediments are tens or hundreds of millions of years old.

Most Quaternary sediments, therefore, owe their genesis in one way or another to the action or melting of ice. In the last 130,000 years, Ireland was covered by ice for long periods. The last glaciation (or ice age) occurred between 73,000 years ago and 10,000 years ago. This had a huge influence on both the landscape and underlying geology of the country. Since 10,000 years ago the action of modern rivers and the infilling of lakes, along with the formation of peat bogs and development of beaches and other coastal features, have been the main natural processes affecting both our landscape and geology.

Glacier in Iceland.

Glaciation in Ireland.

Processes of sediment deposition in the Quaternary Period occurred under glacial, periglacial and temperate conditions and are, by their very nature, fragmentary in their geological record. Thus glacial geologists usually work with sediments which do not have an obvious order of alternating glacial\interglacial events. There is direct evidence in Ireland of no more than two glacial stages and one interglacial stage. There were almost certainly more, but because of the destructive power of ice sheets, much of the evidence has been removed. Ireland has, though, a very rich legacy of geological deposits and physical features relating to the most recent glaciation. Over 90% of Ireland is covered by material deposited during this time.

This glaciation started about 73,000 years ago and lasted until 10,000 years ago, when our climate warmed again. (10,000 years is not so long ago when you consider that Newgrange is 6,000 years old). The maximum extent of the ice occurred sometime between 22,000 years ago and 20,000 years ago, when it covered virtually the whole country. In most areas only the highest mountain peaks stuck up above the ice. This ice was constantly on the move, being fed by snow in its high central area and melting at its margins. Ice moves under its own weight; something like wet concrete will if it is piled on top of itself.

Many of the glacial deposits in the Boyne Valley were laid down during the last glaciation when this area was completely smothered by ice. Ice flow over the region was generally from the northwest to the southeast, although the area along the coast was affected by ice flowing

(Colman Gallagher)

Ice sheet in Alaska. The mountains protrude through the ice like islands. Much of Ireland would have looked like this during the last glaciation.

east to west from the Irish Sea Basin. The deposits in the Boyne Valley which remain from this glaciation are varied in their sedimentology and their landform expression. This suite of landforms and internal sedimentary structures gives hints as to the events which took place during the last glaciation.

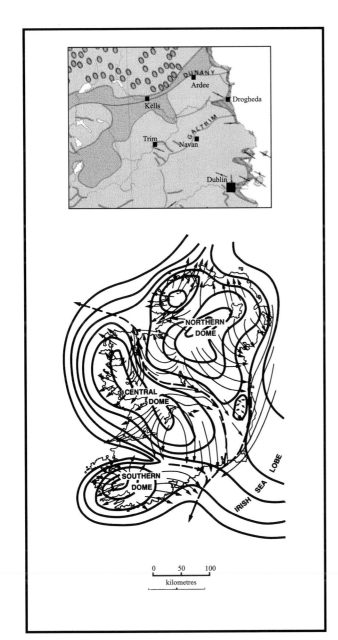

The extent and pattern of ice in Ireland during the last glaciation. The Irish Ice Sheet was made up of three major domes of ice and a number of minor ones. The top diagram shows a general glacial geology of the Boyne Valley, with drumlins in the north of the area, a broad band of hummocks and gravel hills below that and a till plain with some eskers in the south.

How Glaciers Work.

A glacier will form whenever a sufficiently large body of snow accumulates, compacts, and turns into ice. The length of time needed to form a glacier will depend on the rate at which the snow accumulates and turns to ice. If this accumulation rate is high and the loss due to melting is low then the

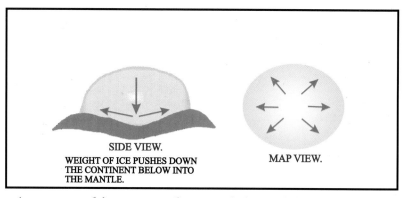

SIDE VIEW.
WEIGHT OF ICE PUSHES DOWN
THE CONTINENT BELOW INTO
THE MANTLE.

MAP VIEW.

As snow and ice accumulates and the weight increases, the ice is forced to flow horizontally, the ice flows radially away from the centre of the ice cap.

glacier will form quickly. When established, its survival will depend on the balance between accumulation and ablation (melting). Glaciers are by no means static masses of ice but have an inherent internal motion. Even glaciers with a retreating margin are constantly moving outwards from their source area: the fact that the margin is retreating only reflects the fact that ablation exceeds accumulation on the glacier as a whole. The zone of accumulation is the 'weight' which drives the glacier forward. A glacier is therefore like a giant conveyor belt, constantly moving ice and rocks towards its toe.

As ice moves out towards its margins, pieces of rock and soil over which it flows become attached to its base by freezing on, and they may become incorporated into the lower layers of the ice. This in turn makes the base of the glacier very abrasive. It can then rapidly erode the underlying material. In this way the substrate is eroded, picked up and transported by the ice. The erosion reduces the level of land underneath the ice sheet where erosion takes place, and increases it by deposition at, or close to, the ice sheet margin. When the ice melts, the transported material is left in one of the many landforms caused by glacial ice. Thus rocks can be carried far away from their source and left as erratics, either at the surface or incorporated into the subsurface. Many of the subsurface erratics also show striae, or scratches, etched into the stones during transportation by the ice.

Ice sheet in Iceland

Glacial meltwater, derived from the melting of ice, is a very important part of the glacial system. It is the main ablation product of ice sheets and is an important lubricant in facilitating glacier movement over rock surface. It is responsible for moving debris from the ice and carrying it beyond the glacier margin. Melting occurs on the surface of the ice, within a glacier and at the base of the ice.

Energy for the melting of ice is supplied by solar radiation (sunlight), friction due to ice flow or heat derived from the Earth's crust beneath the glacier. The surface melting of ice is probably the most important contribution to glacial meltwater. As it results from warm air temperatures its production is highly seasonal with the majority of the meltwater being produced in summer.

Glacier terminating in a lake in Iceland. Note the dark band in the centre of the ice, which is a medial moraine

Legacy of the Ice

When the ice sheets of the Last Ice Age melted, they left a striking record of their actions imprinted on the Irish Landscape. In some areas remnants of erosion are visible, elsewhere thick blankets of ground-up rocks, which were formerly carried by the ice, have been spread across the landscape in a variety of forms. Here we will look at the legacy of erosion and deposition.

At the maximum extent of glaciation ice covered the entire Boyne Valley and was over 400m thick. As the ice flowed over the ground loose debris became incorporated into its base and was also sheared up into the ice sheet itself. These subsequently acted as scouring agents (like the grains in sandpaper) as described above and eroded, polished and moulded the landscape into the forms which we see today. Striae are grooves or scratches which were cut into bedrock by rock particles embedded in the ice which passed over it. Striae are often found on bedrock outcrops in the Boyne Valley, *e.g.* Corballis Hill near Kilberry. These are aligned along the plane of ice movement and are therefore an excellent indicator of past ice movements.

Roches moutonnées are another indicator of ice flow direction. These are moulded rock forms generally polished on the up-ice side (direction from which the ice flowed), and plucked on the down-ice (lee) side. Such polished rock forms are frequently found on the higher ridges in the north of the Boyne Valley area, *e.g.* the ridges around Collon.

The ice, while crossing the area, also carried erratics far from their source, notably granite from the Bellananagh area of County Cavan. This is commonly found as large blocks strewn across the lowland in the northwest of the Boyne Valley, as well as in the subsoil of that area.

Material eroded from the underlying surface was therefore drawn into the ice, transported for a distance and redeposited elsewhere. A portion of each type of rock

Striated limestone clast from a till section near Navan

Erratic of sandstone on the summit of Slieve na Calliagh, the highest point in the Boyne Valley. The sandstone has been transported from the northwest and placed here by the ice. The ridge itself is made up of greywacke and siltstone rocks

in transport was ground down to its smallest constituent grain size. Therefore, the physical composition of the resultant glacial sediments (tills) are often linked to the underlying bedrock which the ice has passed over. For example, the tills around Moynalty are very clayey as much of the bedrock in that area is very fine grained. The debris entrained in the ice was eventually deposited either directly by

(Colman Gallagher)

Debris (till) being deposited from ice in a cavity under a glacier in Alaska.

the ice as this till (boulder clay), or by glacial meltwaters as gravel, sand, silt or clay. The thickness of the glacial deposits and their surficial expression varies greatly over the area. The glacial deposits are usually at their thinnest in the upland areas where bedrock frequently outcrops On the lowlands till thicknesses in excess of 50 m have been recorded in central Meath.

Where there are thick glacial sediments they may take the form of drumlins. Drumlins are elongate hills generally composed of till deposited beneath a moving ice mass. Their characteristic shape gave the feature its name which is derived from the Irish *droimnín* (small, round-backed hill). Drumlins are glacially streamlined with their long axes in line with ice flow direction. The northern area of the Boyne Valley is characterised by drumlin swarms. The drumlins are usually tens of metres high and several hundred metres long. One of the effects that these features have on the area is to influence the local drainage pattern, resulting in poorly drained land in the inter-drumlin zones relative to the steeper drumlin slopes. In the northern part of the Boyne Valley lakes often occupy these badly drained, inter-drumlin areas.

The orientation of the drumlins gives us good indication of the direction of ice flow throughout the region. Around Drumconrath, Nobber and Moynalty they are all oriented northwest to southeast, indicating a former ice flow in that direction.

Glacial debris were frequently deposited at the ice margin as accumulations of tills, gravels, sands, silts or clays in the form of ridges called moraines. In the Irish context the most important are terminal moraines, which are left where ice melts at the snout of an ice sheet. The features often have a steep slope on one side, which is a record of the face which the ice had contact with (ice-contact face). Moraines occur in various guises throughout the Boyne Valley area, but those along the southern side of Slieve na Calliagh around Diamor/Ballinlough are particularly impressive. These are aligned southwest-northeast and illustrate the position of a temporarily stabilised ice margin as the ice melted back across the area during deglaciation.

Drumlins in Ballyhoe townland, north Meath. Note the consistent orientation of the features.

Many of the lakes in the Boyne Valley owe their origin to glacial action. Although classic U-shaped valleys are not present in the Boyne Valley area, long, linear depressions have been gouged out in the west of the area which contain lakes such as Lough Bane, Lough Glore, Lough Lene and White Lough. Lakes such as Lough Sheelin, Lough Ramor, Ben Loughs and Loughs Naneagh are a result of ice erosion and deposition acting together. Mullagh Lough and Whitewood and Newcastle Loughs in the Kingscourt Valley are held up by moraines. Drumlins impound most of the other lakes in the area, such as Lough Bracken, Ballyhoe Lough, Breakey

Lough Naneagh in western County Meath. The lake is surrounded by hills composed of till or gravels and is hence dammed by these glacially derived deposits

Lough, Ervey Lough, Corstown Loughs, Mentrim Lough and Mullagh Lough, and the many smaller lakes interspersed with the drumlin landforms.

The Record of Meltwater during Deglaciation

Glaciofluvial sands and gravels are deposited by meltwater streams flowing from a melting glacier. They are usually well sorted, with the gravels often rounded. As these sediments are the final imprint left on the landscape during latter stages of glaciation (this is the period of *de*glaciation during which the ice finally disintegrated), meltwater deposits are very common in the Boyne Valley. They occur as a variety of landforms, each laid down in a different way by meltwater issuing from the ice.

Eskers are long, sinuous ridges composed of sands and gravels which were laid down by subglacial streams in tunnels under the ice sheet. When the ice melts the esker

Outwash river in front of a glacier in Iceland. See the vast amounts of gravel being deposited by the river.

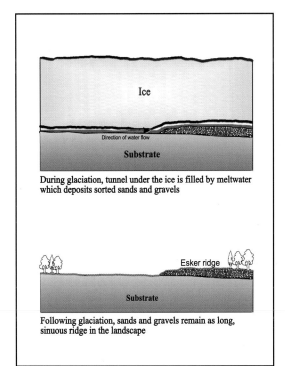

Ice

Direction of water flow

Substrate

During glaciation, tunnel under the ice is filled by meltwater which deposits sorted sands and gravels

Esker ridge

Substrate

Following glaciation, sands and gravels remain as long, sinuous ridge in the landscape

Diagram showing the formation of an Esker

Esker ridge at Castletown, north Meath

ridge provides a 'standing record' of the former river under the ice. There are many fine examples of esker gravels sorted and deposited by glacial meltwaters in the Trim area, as well as further north around Castletown and Kells.

Deltas are formed as sediment is deposited at a river mouth on entry into a glacial lake. These usually contain interbedded sands and gravels which dip or incline sharply lakeward. The deltas are left as hills of sand and gravel when the ice melts and the lake drains away. The finer sediments, such as clay and silt, were carried out into the deeper and more

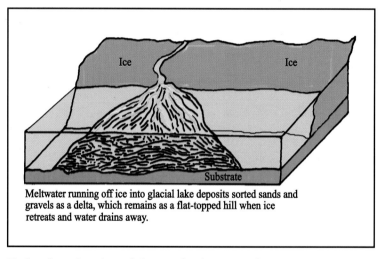

Meltwater running off ice into glacial lake deposits sorted sands and gravels as a delta, which remains as a flat-topped hill when ice retreats and water drains away.

Delta forming in a lake at the ice margin

distant parts of the lake. These are usually found in extensive depressions (flat areas) in today's landscape and often facilitate the development of peat bogs owing to their badly drained nature. Delta sands and gravels are present at Coghalstown (near Wilkinstown), at Ricetown near Lobinstown and again extensively in the Trim area. Substantial occurrences of fine sand and silt around Fletcherstown and Ladyrath Bogs and in the Dunderry area were deposited into ice-dammed lakes at the southern part of the retreating ice margin.

Sandar (plural of the Icelandic *sandur,* meaning outwash river) are sheets of outwash gravel which have been deposited by wide, braided meltwater rivers in a broad zone in front of a melting ice sheet. These sheets of gravel may pass over and around terminal moraines and areas which once contained dead, stagnant ice. The sediments consist

Sandur (outwash river) in front of a glacier in iceland. The photo is taken from the top of the glacier (note ice in the foreground).

of well sorted sands and gravels. On the surface sandar may be very flat (as is the case in east County Meath, around Gormanston) or very hummocky (as is the case in the Blackwater Valley around Carnaross). There are large spreads of sandur gravels along the Boyne itself east of Navan, around Gormanston, around Castletown and in the Moynalty and Blackwater Valleys.

Kames are formed in depressions on the top of a glacier and in other cavities within the ice. As the ice melts the sands and gravels which accumulate in the cavities are 'let down' onto the land surface causing an irregular mound or knob. The gravels are rounded and sorted, a result of water running through the cavities in the ice. Kames are often seen in association with kettle holes, which are rounded

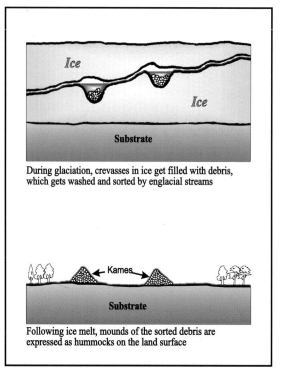

During glaciation, crevasses in ice get filled with debris, which gets washed and sorted by englacial streams

Following ice melt, mounds of the sorted debris are expressed as hummocks on the land surface

Diagram showing the formation of a kame

Kame at Murrens, western County Meath

depressions left when (sometimes buried) blocks of dead ice among the deposited debris melt. Hummocky, pitted landscapes are thus described as having kame and kettle topography. In the Boyne Valley the kames are usually no more than 10m high

The Delvin Meltwater Channel, near Gormanstown in east County Meath

and tens of metres in diameter. A kame and kettle landscape occurs extensively south of Oldcastle around Murrens. Kames occur between drumlins in several places in north Meath, notably around Kilmainhamwood at the base of the Kingscourt Valley.

Meltwater erosion has cut some spectacular meltwater channels in the area. These channels are deeply cut and usually house streams much smaller than would be expected for the channel (misfit streams). The Boyne Channel itself is a rock-cut meltwater channel (meaning it has been incised into bedrock along much of its course). Many of the Boyne's tributary channels east of Slane, the Nanny Channel and the Delvin Channel are other good examples.

More 'modern' geology

The Boyne alluvial flat, Kilcarn, Navan.

More recently, in the Holocene Epoch, the warmer climate effected a large change in the environment. The development of the modern fluvial systems was largely controlled by the pre-existing glacial landscape. The floors of these modern valleys take the form of alluvial floodplains. The Boyne River has a wide floodplain along much of its course resulting from the deposition of alluvium as the river has meandered across its valley.

The change in climatic conditions also resulted in the growth of peat (bog). Blanket bog is associated with highland areas where poor drainage enabled the build-up of oxygen-starved, partially decomposed biomass. This is not found in the Boyne Valley area. **Raised bogs** developed in many small lake basins, spreading over time to the

Marsh at Clonycurry near Trim. It is under such conditions that peat forms

surrounding land. These occur extensively in west County Meath and many are exploited by Bord na Móna *e.g.* Ballivor and Coolronan Bogs, Bohermeen Bog. Smaller areas of raised bog are frequently found in inter-drumlin areas in the north of the Boyne Valley, such as the hollows around Moynalty and Drumconrath.

The modern coastline began to develop after the postglacial sea-level stabilised at its present level more than 5,000 years ago. In that period the modern beaches (*e.g.* Bettystown, Laytown) and spits (*e.g.* Mornington) were formed and blown sand collected in the form of sand dunes. The accumulation of these sediments is balanced by the erosion of other components of the coast line, and the slumps along the cliffs in glacial deposits backing the beaches bear testament to ongoing erosion of much of the coast in this area. The straight coastline south of Drogheda is related to the fact that the Quaternary sediments in this area are relatively soft glacial deposits rather than harder, more resistant bedrock (compare with the craggy planform of the north Dublin coastline).

The Boyne Valley before glaciation

The Boyne Valley is situated in the northeastern part of the Central Plain of Ireland. The southern half of the valley generally lies at between 30m and 120m above sea level and forms a gently undulating lowland plain, broken intermittently by bedrock cored hills. In the northern half of the valley elevations rise quite steeply and the landscape is much more varied, with high bedrock-cored hills west of Kells and north of Slane, and drumlins in the area north of these, dominating the topography.

Almost all of the bedrock geology of the Boyne Valley is of Palaeozoic age, comprising a succession of rocks which range in age from the Ordovician to the Triassic, a time span of approximately 250 million years.

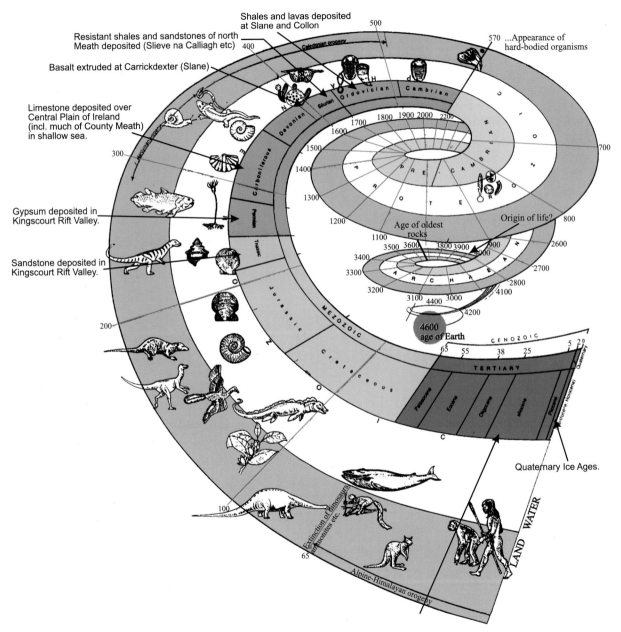

Shales and lavas deposited
at Slane and Collon

Resistant shales and sandstones of north
Meath deposited (Slieve na Calliagh etc)

Basalt extruded at Carrickdexter (Slane)

Limestone deposited over
Central Plain of Ireland
(incl. much of County Meath)
in shallow sea.

Gypsum deposited in
Kingscourt Rift Valley.

Sandstone deposited in
Kingscourt Rift Valley.

...Appearance of
hard-bodied organisms

Origin of life?

Age of oldest
rocks

4600
age of Earth

Quaternary Ice Ages.

LAND WATER

*Subdivisions of geological time, showing major events
in the Earth's geological history.*

62

The oldest rocks in the Boyne Valley are of Ordovician age (505-438 million years ago) and crop out in three areas. The largest area occurs between Slane and Collon, with the rocks consisting of a series of volcanic tuffs and lavas, and some shales. The basalt rocks at Carrickdexter just west of Slane (quarried extensively by Cement Roadstone PLC) are associated with these but are probably a little younger, estimated at Lower Devonian in age (400 million years old). Ordovician rocks are present, but crop out less extensively at surface, around Bellewstown and Fourknocks, and in the northwest of the area just outside Ballyjamesduff (Carn and Kilquilly townlands). These rocks are generally mudrocks and siltstones, interfingering with some volcanic lavas.

Silurian rocks, which are between 438m and 408m years old, outcrop in three areas within the valley. The largest area lies in the northwest and includes the southeast-northwest trending ridges of the Slieve na Calliagh, Ballinlough and Kells areas and extends northwards to the county boundary west of a line between Headfort, Moynalty and Kingscourt. The outcropping rocks consist of shale, siltstone, sandstone and greywacke (impure sandstone). The rocks are much more resistant to erosion than the surrounding Lower Carboniferous rocks, hence the high escarpments at Ballinlough, Slieve na Calliagh, Crossakeel, Screebog and Teevurcher.

An area of Silurian rocks surrounds those of Ordovician age at Collon/Slane/Grangegeeth. The rocks consist of greywackes and black mudrocks and give rise to the high, east-west oriented ridges of the Rathkenny and Collon areas. Similarly oriented ridges of Silurian age in the Bellewstown area are composed of shales, mudrocks and sandstones. These rocks outcrop quite extensively on the crests of the ridges.

Bedrock of Lower Carboniferous age is the most common in the Boyne Valley and consist mostly of limestone. This rock is generally covered by a thick blanket of Quaternary deposits and dominates the southern portion of County Meath as well as north County Kildare, and the area between Kells and Drumconrath in the north. Although pure limestone is normally composed of calcium carbonate ($CaCO_3$), the limestone here also contains marine sands and muds with abundant fossils of shells, coral and sea plants. This reflects the fact that much of Ireland was covered by a shallow sea between 355 and 325 millions years ago. Chert, which is a hard material composed of microcrystalline quartz, occurs in association with some of the Lower Carboniferous limestone. It gives rise to the high craggy hills around Lough Bane, White Lough and Fore.

Upper Carboniferous lithologies comprise the bedrock of small disjunct areas of only a few square kilometres in various parts of the county. They can be found east of the Kingscourt Valley, between Walterstown and Donore, south of Yellow Furze, south of Rathfeigh, between Skyrne and Tara, northeast of Trim and around Moynalvey-Garadice. The rocks are shales and sandstones which were deposited predominantly in deltaic environments and are between 324 and 300 million years old.

The youngest rocks in the area lie just north of the Boyne Valley at the base of the Kingscourt Valley. The rocks consist of red Triassic sandstones which are underlain by Permian gypsum deposits. This gypsum was deposited in lagoonal conditions 290 to 210 million years ago. It has been extensively quarried by Gypsum Industries PLC in recent years.

We have, as yet, no record of any of the geological events which influenced the Boyne Valley area between 210 million years and 2 million years ago. Some of the rocks may have been covered by younger Jurassic or Cretaceous rocks but any cover of newer material would have been removed during the Tertiary Period (66.4 million - 1.6 million years ago) that followed. We do know that during the Tertiary much of the present surface form of Ireland began to appear. The onset of the Quaternary Period brought with it the dramatic change in climate which produced long periods of very cold conditions which reduced vegetation to a thin tundra cover and eventually saw the development of the great ice sheets. It was this periodic glacial activity over the last 1.6m years which put the finishing touches to the emerging landscape of the Boyne Valley.

Glaciation and Deglaciation in the Valley Area.

The Boyne Valley was influenced by ice from two sources: the north central midlands and the Irish Sea Basin. The evidence for glaciation, and the exact pattern of glacial movement and deposition, is interpreted from geological and geomorphological features: essentially the composition and the stratigraphy (layering) of the glacial and meltwater sediments and their surface shape. This guide highlights the most striking glacial features in the landscape, but it should be borne in mind that the interpretation of the glacial history is based on the total geological record.

There is a great variety of glacial and glaciofluvial deposits across the area of the Boyne Valley. The direct glacial deposits are very varied in their composition. Most of the sediments are dominated by limestone debris, but in many areas in the north and east of the valley they are derived from Lower Palaeozoic rocks, mostly shales and sandstones. Generally the glacial deposits dominated by Lower Palaeozoic rocks overlie bedrock of Lower Palaeozoic age. Many of the sediments contain high proportions of far travelled erratics. For example, sediments include basalt erratics from Carrickdexter many kilometres south of Slane, granite from Bellananagh in Cavan is found around Oldcastle and Triassic sandstone erratics from Kingscourt are present as far south as Nobber. All of the erratics suggest a former ice movement from the northwest to southeast which conforms with the orientation of drumlins and striae which also occur in the area.

The dominant grain-size found in the tills is partly a reflection of the underlying bedrock. In the north of the valley, much of the tills are clayey or silty, resulting in relatively poor drainage (often reflected in the natural vegetation). This is due to the fact that much of the underlying bedrock in this area is of shale or siltstone, and during glaciation these rocks were ground down to their constituent particles by the ice resulting in a clayey subsoil texture. South of Navan the land is better drained generally. The tills here are more often silty to sandy, and usually quite stony, which results in better drainage. The stony nature of the tills reflects the resistance of the underlying (relatively hard) limestone to crushing by the ice during glaciation.

The most striking glacial deposit near the coast is a clayey till which usually contains marine shell fragments and flints, as well as other erratics from the northern Irish Sea Basin. This till was laid down by the ice sheet which occupied the Irish Sea Basin while it moved onshore. In places this deposit contains erratics of Ailsa Craig microgranite, which has been carried from the Firth of Clyde in Scotland. The till is well exposed around Ben Head and as far south as Gormanston, where it is overlain by sorted sands and gravels (clearly seen in the cliff sections along the beach).

The precise relationship between the two ice sheets which affected the Boyne Valley area is difficult to decipher. Erratics from the Irish Sea Basin have been found as far inland as Slane and shells occur in sands near Naul but we cannot tell exactly how far inland the Irish Sea Glacier reached.

Irish Sea Till in an exposure at Ben Head just south of Laytown. See the tightly packed nature of the till, reflecting the fact that it was placed under an ice sheet several hundred metres thick.

The inland ice had a source in the Leitrim/Fermanagh area and moved over the Valley area in a northwest to southeast direction. During the onset of deglaciation as this ice thinned, the presence of high, bedrock ridges (such as Slieve na Calliagh) strongly influenced the direction of ice movement, especially in northern areas. As erratic blocks of sandstone are strewn across the crest of the Slieve na Calliagh ridge (the highest point in the Boyne Valley area, and underlain by shale and greywacke), we know that the entire area was covered by ice during the glacial maximum. The blocks have been transported by the ice from the northwest and perched on top of the feature.

After the ice sheets began to melt they separated close to the present coastline and much of the meltwater escaped southwards to the sea. A wide river existed in the Gormanston/Ben Head area which is reflected in the vast amounts of gravels there today. These are clearly seen in Murphy's Pit just off the N1. Bedded sands and gravels here reflect deposition by meandering streams laden with sediment. Most of the stones in these pits are of limestone, but some erratic flint occurs.

At this point the Irish Sea ice ceased to have an effect on land and continued to retreat northwards up the Irish Sea Basin towards its source in Scotland and northeastern Ireland. The inland ice sheet melted back across the countryside towards the centres of the ice dome in the Leitrim/Fermanagh area. Many of the moraines which straddle the Boyne Valley are aligned southwest to northeast indicating that the ice margin was oriented in this direction during retreat.

Glossary of technical terms

Terms underlined have their own entry in the glossary.

Alluvium (n.): sediments deposited by fluvial (river) processes. **Alluvial** (adj.).

Argillaceous (adj.): term describing a <u>sedimentary rock</u> with an average grain size less than 1/16mm; <u>clays</u>, <u>silts</u>, mudstones *etc.*.

Basalt (n.): dark, fine grained <u>igneous</u> rock, rich in iron and magnesium but with little or no <u>quartz</u>.

Basic (adj.): applied to <u>quartz</u>-free <u>igneous</u> rock, rocks low in silica.

Bed (n.): a single unit of a <u>sediment</u>, distinct from those on either side.

Bedding (n.): arrangement of a <u>sediment</u> in layers of varying thickness and character.

Bedrock (n.): unweathered rock below the cover of un<u>lithified</u> deposits.

Braided (adj.): branching and joining repeatedly to form an intricate network.

Calcareous (adj.): *i.e.* containing calcium carbonate ($CaCO_3$).

Chert (n.): hard material composed of microcrystalline <u>quartz</u> or opaline silica; occurs as nodules or <u>beds</u> in <u>limestone</u>. **Cherty** (adj.).

Clast (n.): any particle above 2mm across derived from pre-existing rock.

Clay (n.): a <u>sediment</u> of particle size less than 0.002mm. **Clayey** (adj.).

Cross bedding (n.): layers in a <u>sediment</u> inclined at an angle to the general orientation of <u>bedding</u>. These generally reflect the depositional surfaces within wave or wind ripples or dunes. **Cross bedded** (adj.).

Cryoturbations (n.): irregular structures resulting from the displacement of soil horizons under cryostatic pressure, within soils in a <u>periglacial</u> climate.

Dead-ice topography (n.): undulating landscape in which a disordered assemblage of knolls, mounds or ridges of glacial deposits with irregular depressions, pits or <u>kettles</u> that are commonly undrained and which may contain ponds or peat.

Deglaciation (n.): the period of time during which there is a net melting of ice, rather than a net accumulation and spreading out of ice *i.e.* the time during which climate is returning to an <u>interglacial</u> one.

Delta (n.): <u>fan</u>-shaped plain of <u>alluvial</u> <u>sediments</u> at river mouth upon entry into the sea or a lake which is crossed by many distributaries, often extending beyond the general trend of the coastline or lake-shore. **Deltaic** (adj.).

Dip (n.): the maximum angle of inclination of a <u>sedimentary</u> <u>bed</u> or planar fabric. **Dipping** (v.).

Drumlin (n): low smooth, elongate, streamlined hill composed of glacial deposits.

Drumlinoid (adj.): assuming certain characteristics of a <u>drumlin</u> but not fully streamlined.

Erratic (n.), (adj.): rock moved by glacial or floating ice from its original outcrop.

Escarpment (n.): a steep slope or cliff on one side of a hill or ridge with sides of varying slope angle.

Esker (n.): long narrow sinuous ridge of <u>sand</u> and <u>gravel</u> deposited by a <u>subglacial</u> stream and left behind after the ice melted.

Extrusive (adj.): referring to an <u>igneous</u> rock emplaced at, rather than beneath, the Earth's surface.

Fan (n.): fan-shaped mass of <u>sediments</u> which have been deposited by <u>fluvial</u> processes; may be formed in a variety of situations and settings.

Fault (n.): planar fracture in <u>sediments</u> across which there has been some displacement; commonly inclined but may be vertical. *Normal fault*: a fault in which the hanging wall has moved downward relative to the footwall. *Reverse fault*: a fault in which the hanging wall has moved upward relative to the footwall. *Wrench fault*: a fault in which the <u>sediments</u> on either side have moved laterally relative to each other. **Faulted** (adj.).

Fold (n.): a curve or bend of any planar structure such as rock strata. **Folded** (adj.).

Geology (n.): the science of the Earth: how it was formed, what it is made of, its history and the changes that take place on it and in it. **Geological, Geologic** (adj.).

Geomorphology (n.): the study of landforms; the study of the surface forms of the Earth and their development. **Geomorphological** (adj.).

Glacial debris (n.): material being transported by a glacier in contact with glacier ice.

Glaciation (n.): the actions of glaciers and ice sheets including glacial erosion and deposition. Term also used to describe a period of time in the Earth's history when ice in the form of glaciers spread into areas that were free from it at other times. **Glaciated** (adj.).

Glaciofluvial (adj.): of or pertaining to rivers made up of meltwater from glaciers or ice sheets.

Glaciolacustrine (adj.): of or pertaining to lakes made up of meltwater from glaciers or ice sheets. These lakes may or may not be dammed on one or more sides by the ice itself.

Granite (n.): pale, coarsely crystalline intrusive <u>igneous</u> rock, comprising mostly <u>quartz</u> and feldspar.

Gravel (n.): a <u>sediment</u> with particle size over 2.0mm. **Gravelly** (adj.).

Hillocks (n.): small hills.

Hummocks (n.): small irregular-shaped hills, generally occurring in clusters.

Ice-contact face (n.): steep slope on an <u>ice marginal</u> landform located in the place where the ice once supported the feature.

Ice margin (n.): the edge of an ice sheet or glacier. **Ice marginal** (adj.), **Ice marginally** (adv.).

Ice oscillation (n.): a fluctuation in the position of the <u>ice margin</u> caused by a forward movement of the ice, followed by a retreat. This may be repeated several times.

Ice stagnation (n.), (adj.): the decay of ice; and pertaining to this decay. Also **ice wastage**.

Ice stream (n.): a body of ice which moves independently of (and usually faster than) the rest of an ice sheet; this may be caused by troughs in the bed which channel fast flow, or the occurrence of soft, deformable <u>sediment</u> under the ice.

Ice wedge casts (n.): crack infilled with soil which has resulted from the intense freeze-thaw processes of a <u>periglacial</u> climate.

Igneous (adj.): rock solidified from magma; may be <u>extrusive</u> or <u>intrusive</u>.

Interglacial (n.), (adj.): the time interval between glacial stages; pertaining to this time.

Intrusive (adj.): <u>igneous</u> rock emplaced within the Earth's crust. **Intrusion** (n.).

Irish Sea Till (n.): <u>clay</u>-rich till found along the eastern seaboard of Ireland, and occurring as much as 12km inland, which was deposited by an ice stream which occupied the Irish Sea Basin during the last <u>glaciation</u>.

Kame (n.): mound, knob or ridge of <u>stratified</u> <u>sand</u> and <u>gravel</u> deposited by a <u>subglacial</u> stream. **Kamiform** (adj.): kame-like.

Kame terrace (n.): terrace which is a remnant of a stream bed that has formed along a valley wall at an <u>ice margin</u>, usually composed of <u>stratified</u> <u>sand</u> and <u>gravel</u>.

Kame and kettle topography (n.): hummocky, disorganised landscape composed of numerous hillocks of <u>sand</u> and <u>gravel</u> interspersed with <u>kettle holes</u>.

Kettle hole (n.): rounded depression left behind when a (sometimes buried) block of 'dead' ice from an ice sheet melts.

Karst (n.): <u>topographic</u> features formed by solution of rock, usually <u>limestone</u>, by surface water or groundwater, including sink holes, caves and underground drainage. **Karstic, Karstified** (adj.).

Lacustrine basin (n.): a generally rounded, relatively shallow depression which once held, or still holds, a lake. **Lacustrine** (adj.) is a term referring to <u>sediments</u> and processes of or pertaining to lakes.

Lava (n.): general term for molten extrusive material, or the rock solidified from it.

Limestone (n.): <u>sedimentary rock</u> composed of calcium carbonate, often containing fossils.

Lithification (n.): process whereby <u>sediments</u> are transformed into solid rocks. **Lithified** (adj.).

Lithology (n.): rock type. **Lithological** (adj.), **Lithologically** (adv.).

Lodgement (n.), (adj.): process by which debris is released from the sliding base of a moving glacier/ice sheet and plastered or 'lodged' onto the glacier bed; also describes <u>tills</u> emplaced by this process (**lodgement till**).

Matrix (n.): fine-grained material filling the spaces between the larger grains in a <u>sediment</u>.

Melt-out (n.), (adj.): process by which <u>glacial debris</u> is very slowly released from ice that is not sliding or deforming internally; also describes <u>tills</u> emplaced by this process.

Meltwater Channel (n.): deeply cut drainage channel which is a result of meltwater erosion during <u>ice wastage</u>.

Misfit stream (n.): a stream which is too small to have eroded the valley in which it flows. Often the case with streams now flowing in <u>meltwater channels</u>.

Moraine (n.): mound or ridge of unsorted and un<u>stratified</u> <u>glacial debris</u>, deposited commonly at the <u>ice margin</u>. **Morainic** (adj.). *Terminal moraine/end-moraine*: a moraine left where the ice melts at the lower end, or margin, of a glacier or ice sheet. *Lateral moraine*: a moraine formed by rock material falling on the sides of a glacier from the sides of the valley.

Morphology (n.): the form and structure of the land surface in an area or place. **Morphological** (adj.), **Morphologically** (adv.).

Outwash (adj.): synonymous with <u>glaciofluvial</u> (of or pertaining to rivers made up of meltwater from glaciers or ice sheets). Hence *outwash fans*, *outwash plains* and *outwash terraces*.

Oxidation (n.): <u>weathering</u> process involving combination with oxygen. A particularly important oxidation process is the alteration of iron from the ferrous, reduced state, to the ferric, oxidised state:

$$4FeO + O_2 \rightarrow 2Fe_2O_3$$

This process is especially common in rocks rich in mafic minerals, such as <u>shale</u>, and can frequently be observed by the presence of brown iron-staining along cracks and between mineral grains.

Peat (n.): an accumulation of partially decomposed vegetable matter at the Earth's surface.

Periglacial (adj.): refers to the area on the borders of an ice sheet. The word 'periglacial' is used both for the geographical area and for the physical conditions in it which often occur very far from glacial ice. **Periglacially** (adv.).

Permian (n.) (adj.) the period of geological time from 286 million years ago to 245 million years ago.

Proglacial (adj.): in front of a glacier. **Proglacially** (adv.).

Quartz (n.): crystalline silica (SiO_2), very common hard rock-forming mineral.

Quaternary (n.), (adj.): the period of <u>geological</u> time from 1.65 million years ago to the present, subdivided into two Epochs, the Pleistocene and the Holocene; pertaining to that time.

Rogen moraine (n.): <u>subglacial</u> ridge formed transverse to ice flow, with distinctive streamlined upper surfaces. Not to be confused with <u>terminal moraines</u>; rogen moraines are formed *beneath* the ice.

Roche moutonnée (n.): ice-sculpted rock form with elongate, smooth and domed surface, long-axis oriented in direction of ice movement.

Sand (n.): a <u>sediment</u> of particle size between 2.0mm and 0.06mm. **Sandy** (adj.).

Sandur (n.) (*sandar*, *pl.*): a low-angle <u>fan</u> or sheet of <u>outwash</u> <u>gravels</u> deposited in front of an ice sheet.

Sandstone (n.): <u>sedimentary rock</u> with <u>sand</u>-sized grains, commonly of <u>quartz</u>.

Sediment (n.): any material that has been obtained from earlier rocks by denudation, and subsequently redeposited.

Sedimentary rock (n.): <u>lithified</u> accumulation of <u>clast</u>ic, organic, or chemically precipitated mineral grains.

Sedimentology (n.): the study of <u>sediments</u> and their formation. Term also used to describe the geometry of <u>sediments</u>. **Sedimentological** (adj.), **Sedimentologically** (adv.).

Shale (n.): mudstone with closely spaced <u>bedding</u>/parallel partings.

Silt (n.): a <u>sediment</u> of particle size between 0.06mm and 0.002mm. **Silty** (adj.).

Siltstone (n.): <u>sedimentary rock</u> composed of <u>silt</u>-sized particles.

Sphagnum (n.): moss which has a remarkable capacity for capturing and storing rain water, and is generally considered as the primary building block for the growth of <u>peat</u> bogs.

Stratification (n.): the presence of layers or <u>beds</u> in a <u>sediment</u>. **Stratified** (adj.).

Stratigraphy (n.): study of all aspects of the science of <u>sedimentary</u> strata. Term also used for the sequence of rock strata. **Stratigraphical** (adj.), **Stratigraphically** (adv.).

Striae (n.): ice-scratches on rock surfaces caused by debris carried by moving ice. **Striated** (adj.).

Subaqueous (adj.): referring to beneath water. **Subaqueously** (adv.).

Subglacial (adj.): referring to beneath the glacier or ice sheet. **Subglacially** (adv.).

Till (n.): <u>sediment</u> deposited by or from glacier ice; unsorted and un<u>stratified</u>, and generally tightly packed.

Triassic (n.) (adj.) the period of geological time from 245 million years ago to 208 million years ago.

Topography (n.): the surface features of an area or place. **Topographical** (adj.), **Topographically** (adv.).

Volcanic (adj.): pertaining to the activity, structure, or rock types of a volcano.

Weathering (n.): the process by which rocks at or near the surface of the Earth are broken up by the action of wind, rain, and changes in temperature. The effects of plants and animals are usually also included. **Weather** (v.), **Weathered** (adj.).

References And Additional Reading List

For the General Reader:

Aalen, F.H.A., Whelan, K. and Stout, M., 1997. Atlas of the Irish Rural Landscape. Cork University Press.

Aalen, F.H.A., 1978. Man and the Landscape in Ireland. Academic Press, London.

Benn, D.I. and Evans, D.J.A., 1998. Glaciers and Glaciation. Arnold, London.

Bennett, M.R. and Glasser, N.F., 1996. Glacial geology - ice sheets and landforms. Wiley, London.

Bradley, J. (Editor), 1988. Settlement and Society in Medieval Ireland. Boethius Press, Kilkenny.

Edwards, K. and Warren, W., 1985. The Quaternary History of Ireland. Academic Press, London.

Eogan, G., 1986. Knowth. Thames and Hudson, London.

Flanagan, D., 1994. Irish Place Names. Gill and Macmillan, Dublin.

Finch, T.F., Gardiner, M.J., Comey, A. and Radford, T., 1983. Soils of County Meath. Soil Survey Bulletin No.37, National Soil Survey of Ireland.

Hambrey, M. and Alean, J., 1992. Glaciers. Cambridge University Press.

Holland, C.H., 1981. A Geology of Ireland. Scottish Academic Press.

Kennan, P., 1995. Written in Stone. Geological Survey of Ireland.

Mitchell, G.F., 1986. The Shell Guide to reading the Irish landscape. Michael Joseph/Country House.

Mitchell, G.F. and Ryan, M., 1997. Reading the Irish landscape. Townhouse, Dublin.

Ryan, M. (Editor), 1994. Irish Archaeology Illustrated. Country House, Dublin.

Whittow, J.B., 1974. Geology and Scenery in Ireland. Penguin Books.

For the Enquiring Reader:

Andrew, C.J. and Ashton, J.H., 1985. Regional setting, geology and metal distribution patterns of Navan orebody, Ireland. Transactions of the Institute of Mining and Metallurgy, 94B: 66-93.

Ashton, J.H., Downing, D.T. and Finlay, S., 1986. The geology of the Navan Zn-Pb orebody. In: Andrew, C.J., Crowe, S., Finlay, S., Pennell, W.M. and Pyne, J.F. (Editors), Geology and genesis of mineral deposits in Ireland. Irish Association for Economic Geology, pp. 243-259.

Bedrock geology manuscript maps (six inch scale), Geological Survey of Ireland, 1871, 1872, 1873.

Brand, S.F. and Emo, G.T., 1986. A note on Zn-Pb mineralisation near Oldcastle, Co. Meath. In: Andrew, C.J., Crowe, S., Finlay, S., Pennell, W.M. and Pyne, J.F. (Editors), Geology and genesis of mineral deposits in Ireland. Irish Association for Economic Geology, pp. 297-304.

Brenchley, P.J., Harper, J.C., Mitchell, W.I. and Romano, M., 1977. A re-appraisal of some Ordovician successions in eastern Ireland. Proceedings of the Royal Irish Academy, 77B: 65-85.

Charlesworth, J.K., 1939. Some observations on the glaciation of north-east Ireland. Proceedings of the Royal Irish Academy, 45B: 255-295.

Charlesworth, J.K., 1955. The Carlingford Readvance between Dundalk Co. Louth, and Kingscourt and Lough Ramor, Co. Cavan. Irish Naturalists' Journal, 2: 299-302.

Close, M.H., 1867. Notes on the General Glaciation of the rocks in the neighbourhood of Dublin. Journal of the Royal Geological Society of Ireland, 1: 3-13.

Colhoun, E.A. and McCabe, A.M., 1973. Pleistocene glacial, glaciomarine and associated deposits of Mell and Tullyallen townlands, near Drogheda, eastern Ireland. Proceedings of the Royal Irish Academy, 73B: 165-206.

Farrington, A., 1957. The ice age in the Dublin district. Journal of the Institute of Chemists in Ireland, 5: 23- 27.

Hamilton, J., 1852. Notes on the geology of the country about Kingscourt. Journal of the Geological Society of Dublin, 5: 161-164.

Harper, J.C., 1952. The Ordovician rocks between Collon (Co. Louth) and Grangegeeth (Co. Meath). Scientific Proceedings of the Royal Dublin Society, 26: 85-112.

Hill, A.R. and Prior, D.B., 1968. Directions of ice movement in North-east Ireland. Proceedings of the Royal Irish Academy, 66B: 71-84.

Hitzman, M., 1992. Bedrock geological map of the Carboniferous of central Ireland: Sheet 13, Meath. Geological Survey of Ireland, Dublin.

Jackson, J.S., 1965. The Upper Carboniferous (Namurian and Westphalian) of Kingscourt, Ireland. Scientific Proceedings of the Royal Dublin Society, 2: 131-152.

Manistre, B.E., 1952. The Ordovician volcanic rocks between Collon (Co. Louth) and Grangegeeth (Co. Meath). Scientific Proceedings of the Royal Dublin Society, 26: 113-128.

McCabe, A.M., 1971. The glacial geomorphology of eastern counties Meath and Louth, eastern Ireland. Unpublished PhD Thesis, Trinity College, Dublin, 382pp.

McCabe, A.M., 1972. Directions of late Pleistocene ice flows in eastern counties Meath and Louth, Ireland. Irish Geography, 6: 443-461.

McCabe, A.M., 1973. The glacial stratigraphy of eastern counties Meath and Louth. Proceedings of the Royal Irish Academy, 73B: 355-382.

McCabe, A.M., 1985. Geomorphology. In: Edwards, K.J. and Warren, W.P. (Editors), The Quaternary history of Ireland. Academic Press, Dublin, pp. 67-93.

McCabe, A.M. and Dardis, G.F., 1989. A geological view of drumlins in Ireland. Quaternary Science Reviews, 8: 169-177.

McCabe, A.M. and Hoare, P.G., 1978. The late Quaternary history of east central Ireland. Geological Magazine, 115: 397-413.

Meehan, R.T., 1996. Quaternary geology of County Meath. Unpublished final report to Meath County Council on the Quaternary Mapping Programme of 1993-1995, Geological Survey of Ireland, Dublin, 121pp.

Meehan, R.T., 1998. The Quaternary Geology and last glaciation and deglaciation of northwest Meath and adjacent parts of Westmeath and Cavan. Unpublished PhD Thesis, University College Dublin, 504 pp.

Meehan, R.T., Warren, W.P. and Gallagher, C.J.D., 1997. The sedimentology of a late Pleistocene drumlin near Kingscourt, Ireland. Sedimentary Geology, 111: 91-106.

Philcox, M.E., 1984. Lower Carboniferous lithostratigraphy of the Irish Midlands. Irish Association for Economic Geology, Dublin, 84pp.

Romano, M.,1980. The stratigraphy of the Ordovician rocks between Slane (County Meath) and Collon (County Louth), eastern Ireland. Journal of Earth Sciences of the Royal Dublin Society, 3: 53-79.

Stephens, N., Creighton, J.R. and Hannon, A., 1975. The late Pleistocene period in north-eastern Ireland: an Assessment, 1975. Irish Geography, 8: 1-23.

Strogen, P., Somerville, I.D., Pickard, N.A.H. and Jones, G.Ll., 1995. Lower Carboniferous (Dinantian) stratigraphy and structure in the Kingscourt Outlier, Ireland. Geological Journal, 30: 1-23.

Stout, G., 1991. Embanked earthen enclosures in the Boyne Region. Proceedings of the Royal Irish Academy, 91C.

Synge, F.M., 1950. The glacial deposits around Trim, Co. Meath. Proceedings of the Royal Irish Academy, 53B (10): 99-110.

Synge, F.M., 1952. Retreat stages of the last ice sheet of the British Isles. Irish Geography, 2: 168-171.

Synge, F.M. and McCabe, A.M., 1979. Terraces of the Lower Boyne. In: Field Guide to east central Ireland. Irish Association for Quaternary Studies, Dublin, p.12.

Warren, W.P., 1985. Stratigraphy. In: Edwards, K.J. and Warren, W.P. (Editors), The Quaternary history of Ireland. Academic Press, London, pp. 39-65.

Warren, W.P., 1992. Drumlin orientation and the pattern of glaciation in Ireland. Sveriges Geologiska Undersokning, Research Papers, Series Ca 81: 359-366.

Warren, W.P. and Ashley, G.M., 1994. Origins of the ice-contact stratified ridges (eskers) of Ireland. Journal of Sedimentary Research, A64 (3): 433-449.